Maria

THE TEACH YOURSELF BOOKS

BIOCHEMISTRY

TEACH YOURSELF

BIOCHEMISTRY

P. H. JELLINCK
B.A., M.Sc., Ph.D.

Professor and Head of Department of Biochemistry,
Queen's University, Kingston, Ontario, Canada

THE ENGLISH UNIVERSITIES PRESS LTD.
ST. PAUL'S HOUSE   WARWICK LANE
LONDON EC4

First Printed 1954
New Edition 1968

SBN 340 05524

*Made and Printed in Great Britain for the English Universities Press, Ltd., London,
by C. Tinling & Co., Ltd., Liverpool London and Prescot.*

CONTENTS

CONTENTS

INTRODUCTION

BIOCHEMISTRY is the chemistry of living matter; it deals with the chemical processes which go on in both animals and plants and also with the chemical make up of their various components. It is, therefore, related to both physiology, which deals with bodily function, and chemistry, and it has wide application in medicine, industry and agriculture.

Biochemistry is among the newest of the sciences and it has become a subject in its own right, quite separate from physiology or chemistry, only in the last 50 years. Sir Frederick Gowland Hopkins who died recently has sometimes been called the father of modern biochemistry but the contributions of earlier scientists to this subject must be mentioned.

When Wöhler in 1828 synthesized urea, a compound found in large amounts in urine, by the interaction of two inorganic compounds, potassium cyanate and ammonium sulphate, he dealt a death blow to Vitalism. This doctrine maintained that an absolute bar separated organic compounds* from inorganic ones and that organic synthesis in the laboratory was impossible for it could only take place in the living organism. The downfall of Vitalism thus opened the way for the synthesis of a large number of organic compounds many of which occur in plants and animals and it was also shown

---

* Carbon containing compounds usually occurring in animal or vegetable matter but including also substances such as ether, chloroform, etc., which can be prepared in the laboratory and are not found in the living organism.

that there was no special mystery associated with these substances.

Although by 1837 Schwann had already demonstrated that yeast was a living plant-like organism and responsible for the alcoholic fermentation of sugars, it was the research of Pasteur on the souring of wines and milk that did much to elucidate the former phenomenon. He, however, maintained that it was due to the vital activity of yeast and certain micro-organisms which he called ferments. This view had to be modified when the Buchner brothers in 1897 showed that yeast preparations, free from living cells were still capable of fermenting sugars. The substances responsible for this were named enzymes (from the Greek: in yeast) and it has become one of the key words of modern biochemistry.

Another great name in biochemistry is that of Claude Bernard (1813–78). It became recognized from his work that the body not only breaks down foodstuffs to provide energy but also builds up sometimes very complex compounds from them. Thus he showed that the glycogen in liver which acts as a carbohydrate reserve is synthesized by this organ from the glucose in blood. His greatest contribution however was that he recognized the constancy of the human body's internal environment irrespective of the changes in the external medium.

Nearer our time, we may mention F. G. Hopkins who showed that young rats fed on chemically pure food ceased to grow unless minute quantities of fresh milk were added to their diet. He proposed the existence of " accessory food factors " which later became known as vitamins. He is also famous for his work on the production of lactic acid in muscle, his teaching and his recognition of the dynamic aspects of metabolism, i.e. the incessant breakdown and resynthesis of every living body component. This concept has been greatly strengthened by the later work of Schoenheimer using isotope labelled compounds.

Thunberg, Wieland and Warburg in their classical studies of the respiratory enzymes did much towards clearing up the problem of tissue respiration while Lohmann, Engelhardt and Szent Györgyi have done equally good work on the biochemistry of muscular contraction. Szent Györgyi is also the discoverer of Vitamin C.

The names of Meyerhof, Neuberg, Young and the Coris are all associated with the study of alcoholic fermentation and glycolysis, i.e. the breakdown of carbohydrate to lactic acid, and that of Krebs with the formation of urea and the oxidation of lactic acid in the body by cyclic processes. Many more names and biochemical discoveries could be mentioned and in recent years the number of investigators has reached such a proportion that it would be difficult to select a few without doing the others a grave injustice.

There is no doubt whatever that a firm foundation has now been laid for this young science and that the future of of biochemistry looks extremely bright.

CHAPTER I

ELEMENTARY CHEMISTRY

THIS chapter is devoted to the definition of the various chemical terms used in subsequent sections of this book.

The element, the molecule and the atom.

An element is a single substance that cannot be split into anything simpler; it consists of one kind of matter only and no physical or chemical process can make more than one substance from it. Water which is a compound can be split by electrolysis, i.e. passing a current through it, into oxygen and hydrogen, but these are elements and cannot be further subdivided.*

Every element and compound is made up of large numbers of extremely small molecules which themselves consist of atoms. There are over 100 elements known, each denoted by a symbol and the reader need only acquaint himself with about a dozen of these which will be used freely in subsequent chapters.

Element	Symbol	Element	Symbol
Hydrogen	H	Sodium	Na
Carbon	C	Potassium	K
Oxygen	O	Calcium	Ca
Nitrogen	N	Magnesium	Mg
Phosphorus	P	Iron	Fe
Sulphur	S	Iodine	I
Chlorine	Cl		

* The fission of atoms has shown that this statement is not entirely true but for most purposes the original definition of an element is quite satisfactory.

Structure of the atom.

The hydrogen atom which is the simplest one in existence consists of a central positively charged nucleus made up of a proton around which revolves a single negatively charged electron. It is like a sub-atomic solar system.

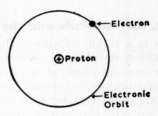

The hydrogen atom.

The proton has unit mass and unit positive charge whereas the electron has unit negative charge but only about 1/1850th the mass of the proton. Thus the hydrogen atom is neutral, as are all atoms, and has an atomic weight of 1, which is the mass of 1 proton; the mass of the electron being negligible. It has also an atomic number of 1, i.e. it has one proton in the nucleus.

The next simplest atom is that of the inert gas helium which has an atomic weight of 4 and an atomic number of 2. This means that there are 2 negatively charged electrons revolving around a doubly charged positive nucleus consisting of two protons and two neutrons which are uncharged particles of the same mass as the proton.

	Charge	*Mass*
2 electrons	2 —	Negligible
2 protons	2 +	2 ←——————atomic number: 2
2 neutrons	0	2
	0	4 ←——————atomic weight: 4

The helium atom

The helium atom is therefore four times as heavy as that of hydrogen and the next atom (atomic number: 3, atomic weight: 7) is heavier still having three protons, three electrons and four neutrons.

The electrons around the nucleus are arranged in a number of different orbits or shells. For the electrons of the first two elements, hydrogen and helium, there is one orbit and then a second wider one for the electrons of the next eight elements, a wider one still for the next eighteen and so on.

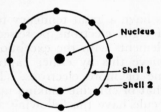

Nucleus

Shell 1
Shell 2

Valency.

Atoms of one element always combine with a definite number of atoms of another element when forming a compound and it is this combining value which is known as valency. In water, one atom of oxygen is combined with two atoms of hydrogen and because the latter has been given a standard valency of 1, the valency of oxygen is 2. One atom of carbon can be found in combination with four atoms of hydrogen as in methane (marsh gas) or with four atoms of the element chlorine and therefore carbon has a valency of 4 and chlorine a valency of 1. In forming carbon dioxide, carbon with a valency of 4 combines with two atoms of oxygen of valency 2.

$$\text{H---O---H} \qquad \text{H---}\overset{\displaystyle H}{\underset{\displaystyle H}{\text{C}}}\text{---H} \qquad \text{O=C=O}$$

water (H_2O)   methane (CH_4)   carbon dioxide (CO_2)

Each line in the formula represents a single bond, i.e. a unit of valency. In the case of carbon dioxide there are two double bonds as that is the only way in which each oxygen atom can be represented as having a valency of 2 and carbon a valency of 4. Triple bonds are also known but are relatively rare.

The ion.

Most atoms have a great tendency to acquire an outer shell of eight electrons possessed by all the stable inert elements with the exception of helium, and they achieve this by either capturing, losing or sharing one or more electrons. The atom of sodium and that of chlorine making up the sodium chloride molecule have the following atomic structure:

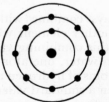

Sodium atom (Na)
1 outer shell electron

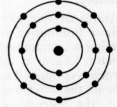

Chlorine atom (Cl)
7 outer shell electrons

Sodium will readily lose its own outer shell electron acquiring an overall positive charge while chlorine readily accepts it and becomes negatively charged.

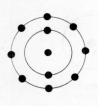

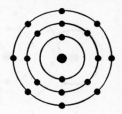

Sodium ion (Na⁺)
8 outer shell electrons

Chlorine ion (Cl⁻)
8 outer shell electrons

Two new electrically charged entities have thus been formed—the sodium ion and the chlorine ion, and whereas positively charged ions are called **cations**, negatively charged ones are known as **anions**.

Electro valency and covalency.

The bond or force holding together sodium chloride (Na—Cl) is said to be electrovalent because the molecule readily forms ions. In fact sodium chloride always exists in the ionized form. The covalent bond is the other main type and in this case the electrons are shared and ions are not formed. By sharing electrons each atom has acquired the outer shell of an inert element (two electrons for helium and eight for the others) and so has formed a stable molecule. There is no charge shift however so that ions are not formed.

Two electrons which are shared are shown graphically as a single bond; four shared electrons as a double bond and six as a triple bond. Thus

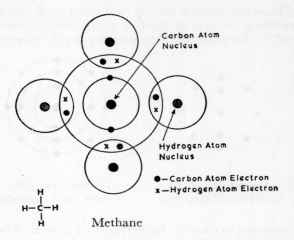

Methane

valency can also be represented in terms of electron sharing capacity and the outer shell electrons of an atom are called the valency electrons.

Acids, alkalis and salts.

Hydrochloric acid (HCl), sulphuric acid (H_2SO_4) and acetic acid (CH_3COOH) are common examples of acids. They are easily recognized by their property of turning the vegetable dye litmus from blue to red and a number of other indicators can also be used for this purpose.

An acid may be better defined however as a compound which gives rise to hydrogen ions (H^+).

$$H_2SO_4 \longrightarrow 2H^+ + SO_4^=$$
Sulphuric acid   hydrogen ions   sulphate ion

Alkalis, on the other hand, give off hydroxyl ions (OH^-) and turn red litmus blue. Caustic soda also known as sodium hydroxide (NaOH) is an example of a well known alkali or base.

$$NaOH \longrightarrow Na^+ + OH^-$$
sodium hydroxide   sodium ion   hydroxyl ion

When an acid and an alkali react they neutralize each other to form a salt (common salt is a typical example) and water.

(1) $H_2SO_4 + 2NaOH \longrightarrow Na_2SO_4 + H_2O$
sodium sulphate (a salt)

acid + base $\longrightarrow$ salt + water

The hydrogen ions have combined with the hydroxyl ions to form water molecules which are neutral and not ionized to any appreciable extent. Equation (1) can be represented more correctly in its ionic form:

$$2H^+ + SO_4^- + 2Na^+ + 2OH^- \longrightarrow$$
$$2Na^+ + SO_4^= + H_2O$$

One molecule of sulphuric acid on ionization gives rise to two hydrogen ions so that two molecules of sodium hydroxide, each of which only gives rise to one hydroxyl ion, will be needed to effect complete neutralization.

Sulphuric acid is called a strong acid and caustic soda a strong base because each is fully ionized. In contrast acetic acid is only partially ionized, i.e. some of the acetic acid molecules exist in equilibrium with acetate ions and hydrogen ions and it is therefore called a weak acid.

$$CH_3COOH \rightleftharpoons CH_3COO^- + H^+$$
acetic acid molecule   acetate ion   hydrogen ion

The symbol $\rightleftharpoons$ denotes a reversible reaction.

Compounds which give rise to hydroxyl ions and

are not fully ionized are weak bases. True salts in solution are almost always completely ionized.

There is one other term in connection with acids and alkalis that must be mentioned—the meaning of the symbol pH. It stands for degree of acidity or alkalinity, all values from 1 to 7 denoting decreasing acidity, 7 itself neutrality and 7–14 increasing alkalinity. The reason for this involves a more thorough knowledge of the quantitative aspects of chemistry than is really needed in this book and the reader is therefore asked to accept it without further explanation.

Oxidation and reduction.

Oxidation may be defined as the addition of oxygen to a substance or the removal of hydrogen from it. The converse, i.e. the addition of hydrogen or the removal of oxygen is called reduction.

$$2\ Cu \quad + \quad O_2 \longrightarrow 2\ CuO$$
copper   oxygen   copper oxide } oxidation
$$H_2S \quad - \quad H_2 \longrightarrow S$$
hydrogen   hydrogen   sulphur
sulphide

The removal of an electron from an ion is also an oxidation and the addition of one—a reduction.

Thus the conversion of ferr*ous* chloride to ferr*ic* chloride is called an oxidation by this definition.

$$2\ FeCl_2 \quad + \quad Cl_2 \longrightarrow 2\ FeCl_3$$
ferr*ous* chloride   chlorine   ferr*ic* chloride

Written in the ionized form ferr*ous* chloride is

$$Fe^{++}\ \begin{matrix} Cl^- \\ Cl^- \end{matrix}\ \text{and ferr}ic\text{ chloride is } Fe^{+++}\ \begin{matrix} Cl^- \\ Cl^- \\ Cl^- \end{matrix}\ \text{so that}$$

Fe^{++} has been converted to Fe^{+++}, i.e. an electron has been removed making the ion more positively charged.

Organic chemistry is the chemistry of carbon compounds. This element, it will be remembered, is tetravalent, and this property enables it to form an almost infinite number of products. Some of the main classes of carbon compounds are given below:

Hydrocarbons.

The saturated hydrocarbons or paraffins are compounds made up of the element carbon and hydrogen only. Methane or marsh gas is the simplest example of this class, the next compound up the scale of complexity being ethane, then propane, then butane and so on.

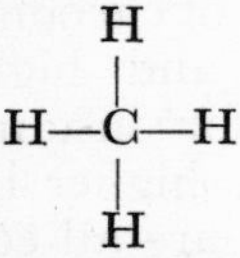

Methane (CH_4) 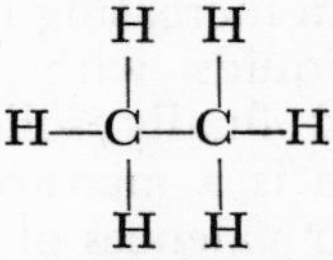   ethane (C_2H_6)

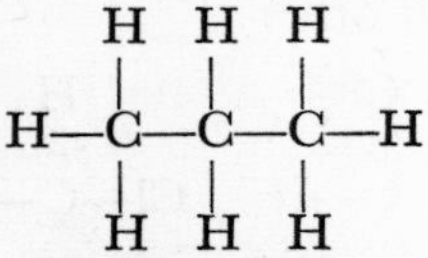

propane (C_3H_8) 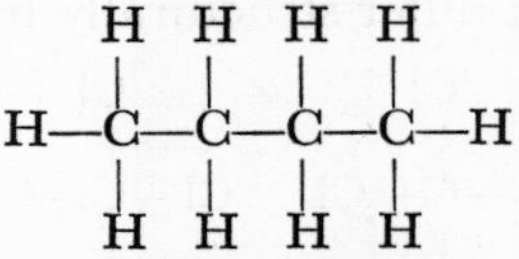   butane (C_4H_{10})

Ethane, propane, and butane can be more conveniently represented as: CH_3CH_3, $CH_3CH_2CH_3$, and $CH_3CH_2CH_2CH_3$ respectively and a series of this kind where each compound differs from the next by having an additional—CH_2—group is called a *homologous series*. All these compounds have their full complement of hydrogen atoms, i.e. they are *saturated*, and they are fairly unreactive chemically. In these examples, the carbon atoms are in a straight line and are therefore called normal or straight chained but butane and the higher members of the series can also occur in a branched form.

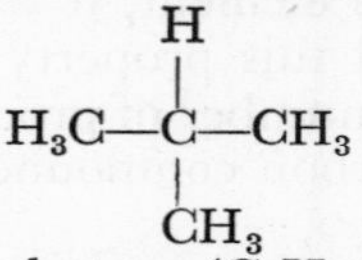

$$\begin{array}{c} H \\ | \\ H_3C-C-CH_3 \\ | \\ CH_3 \end{array}$$

isobutane (C_4H_{10})

The straight chained and branched forms of butane are called *isomers* because though they have the same *molecular formula*, C_4H_{10}, they have different structures. Isomers often have very different physical and chemical properties.

The lower members of the series are all gases but with an increasing number of carbon atoms they become liquids with higher and higher boiling points and finally solids as for instance paraffin wax which is a mixture of the higher homologues.

The four valences of carbon are all equal so that the following compounds are all chloroform and do not differ structurally from each other.

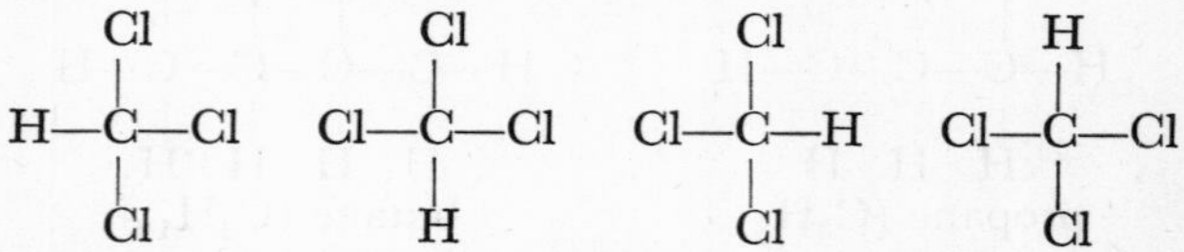

$$\begin{array}{cccc} Cl & Cl & Cl & H \\ | & | & | & | \\ H-C-Cl & Cl-C-Cl & Cl-C-H & Cl-C-Cl \\ | & | & | & | \\ Cl & H & Cl & Cl \end{array}$$

Dichloro substituted methane has no isomers either and

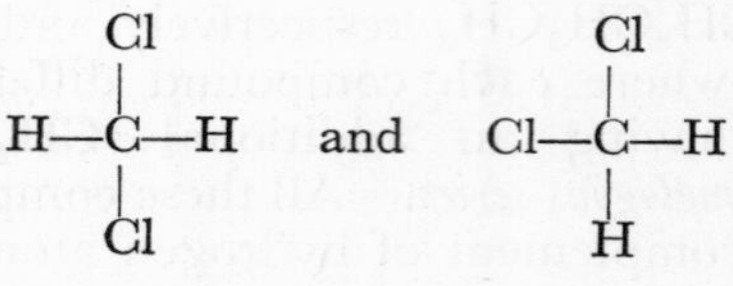

$$\begin{array}{cc} Cl & Cl \\ | & | \\ H-C-H & \text{and} & Cl-C-H \\ | & | \\ Cl & H \end{array}$$

are one and the same compound because though drawn on paper in this manner, the four valences of carbon are in reality directed towards the corners of a regular tetrahedron.

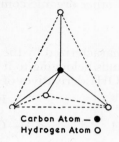

Carbon Atom — ●
Hydrogen Atom ○

Methane

Ethane, however, when dichloro substituted, does have two isomers.

$$\begin{array}{cc} \text{H} & \text{H} \\ | & | \\ \text{H—C—C—H} \\ | & | \\ \text{Cl} & \text{Cl} \end{array} \qquad \begin{array}{cc} \text{H} & \text{H} \\ | & | \\ \text{Cl—C—C—H} \\ | & | \\ \text{Cl} & \text{H} \end{array}$$
(1)   (2)

The unsaturated hydrocarbons can be further sub-divided into those related to ethylene

$$\begin{array}{ccc} \text{H} & & \text{H} \\ & \diagdown \;\; \diagup & \\ & \text{C=C} & \\ & \diagup \;\; \diagdown & \\ \text{H} & & \text{H} \end{array}$$
and those related to acetylene

$HC \equiv HC$ which in contrast to the paraffins are highly reactive chemically. A double and especially a triple bond usually confers great reactivity on a compound.

Petrol and aviation fuels are made up largely from these saturated and unsaturated hydrocarbons and the latter are also very useful as starting material for the synthesis of plastics, synthetic rubber and a large number of other organic compounds.

Alcohols.

This class is characterized by the group —C—OH and the compounds belonging to it may be regarded as hydroxyl (—OH) derivatives of the paraffins.

$$\begin{array}{c} H \\ | \\ H{-}C{-}H \\ | \\ H \\ \text{methane } (CH_4) \end{array} \qquad \begin{array}{c} H \\ | \\ H{-}C{-}OH \\ | \\ H \\ \text{methyl alcohol } (CH_3OH) \end{array}$$

They have a wide occurrence in nature and may be subdivided into three main groups; the primary, secondary and tertiary alcohols. If R stands for a group or *radical* such as methyl (CH_3—) or ethyl (C_2H_5—)

then $\begin{array}{c} H \\ | \\ R{-}C{-}OH \\ | \\ H \end{array}$ is a primary alcohol, $\begin{array}{c} R \\ | \\ R{-}C{-}OH \\ | \\ H \end{array}$

a secondary alcohol and $\begin{array}{c} R \\ | \\ R{-}C{-}OH \\ | \\ R \end{array}$ a tertiary alcohol.

The lower members of the series are liquids and the higher ones solids. Methyl alcohol or methanol CH_3OH, the simplest one known, can be obtained from wood by a process known as destructive distilation.   The wood is heated to a high temperature in the absence of air when methyl alcohol together with other volatile compounds vaporizes and forms a liquid on cooling.   Most methanol these days however is made synthetically by the hydrogenation of carbon monoxide.

$$CO \quad + \quad 2H_2 \longrightarrow CHO_3H$$
$$\text{carbon monoxide}$$

Ethyl alcohol or ethanol, C_2H_5OH, the next one up the series which is responsible for the intoxicating properties of wines and spirits has long been known and is made by fermenting sugars or starch with yeast.   More will be said about this in the chapter on the carbohydrates.

$$\begin{array}{c} CH_2OH \\ | \\ CHOH \\ | \\ CH_2OH \end{array}$$

Glycerol, which has three hydroxyl groups

and is therefore a trihydric alcohol, is another bio-chemically important compound.   It occurs in fats and its phosphate is a breakdown product of glucose in the body.

Carboxylic acids.

These compounds all possess the carboxyl group-

$$\text{ing—COOH or } -C \overset{\displaystyle O}{\underset{\displaystyle OH}{\big\backslash}} \text{ and are acidic because}$$

they give rise to hydrogen ions.

$$RCOOH \longrightarrow RCOO^- + H^+$$

Formic acid, HCOOH, the simplest member, is a very much stronger acid than the others in the series and is responsible for the irritating sting of ants and nettles.

Acetic acid CH_3COOH is vinegar.

Both these compounds have only one carboxyl group but there are several biochemically important acids with two or three of these groups.

Thus succinic acid

$$\text{Thus} \qquad \begin{array}{c} CH_2COOH \\ | \\ CH_2COOH \end{array} \qquad \text{succinic acid}$$

$$\text{and} \qquad HO\!-\!\overset{\displaystyle CH_2COOH}{\underset{\displaystyle CH_2COOH}{\overset{|}{\underset{|}{C}}}}\!-\!COOH \qquad \text{citric acid}$$

are found in the human body where they play a very important role in metabolism.*

Esters.

When organic acids combine with alcohols they form esters.

$$CH_3COOH + HOCH_3 \rightarrow CH_3COOCH_3 + H_2O$$
acetic acid   methanol   methyl acetate

Generally speaking esters are pleasant smelling liquids which are responsible for the flavour and fragrance of many fruits and flowers. The fats are an exception and they are glycerol esters of fatty acids, i.e. the long chain homologues of acetic acid.

* See chapter 2 for the meaning of the word metabolism.

Aldehydes and ketones.

Both these classes have in common the carbonyl group $C=O$, the aldehydes having the general

formula $\overset{R}{\underset{H}{>}}C=O$ and the ketones $\overset{R}{\underset{R}{>}}C=O$. They

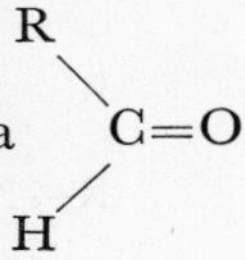

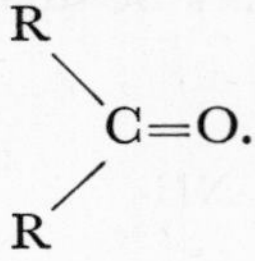

are oxidation products of alcohols; primary alcohols giving aldehydes and secondary alcohols giving ketones.

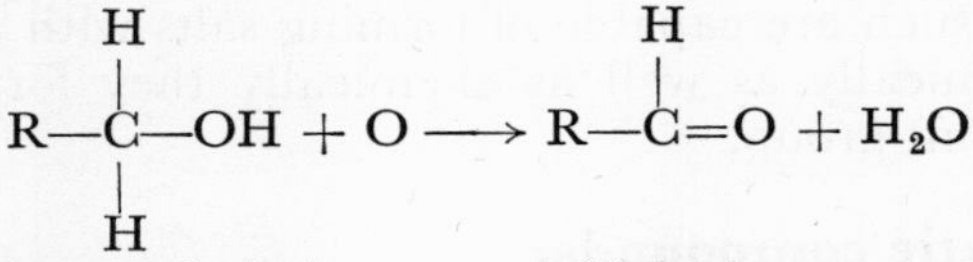

$$R-\overset{H}{\underset{H}{\overset{|}{C}}}-OH + O \longrightarrow R-\overset{H}{\overset{|}{C}}=O + H_2O$$

primary alcohol   aldehyde

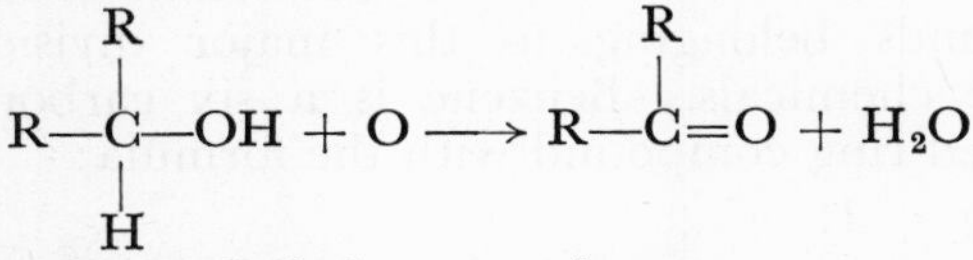

$$R-\overset{R}{\underset{H}{\overset{|}{C}}}-OH + O \longrightarrow R-\overset{R}{\overset{|}{C}}=O + H_2O$$

secondary alcohol   ketone

Aldehydes on further oxidation yield carboxylic acids.

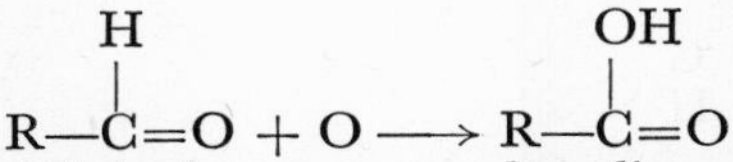

$$R-\overset{H}{\overset{|}{C}}=O + O \longrightarrow R-\overset{OH}{\overset{|}{C}}=O$$

aldehyde   carboxylic acid

Acetaldehyde, CH_3CHO, may be taken as an example of a typical aldehyde and acetone, CH_3COCH_3, that of a typical ketone.

Amines.

The amines are derivatives of ammonia NH_3, which is a pungent gas, fairly alkaline in solution. They may be divided into:

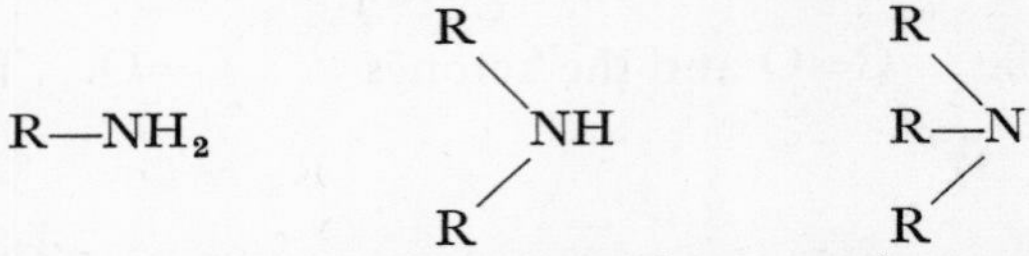

$$R—NH_2 \qquad \begin{matrix} R \\ \diagdown \\ NH \\ \diagup \\ R \end{matrix} \qquad \begin{matrix} R \\ \diagdown \\ R—N \\ \diagup \\ R \end{matrix}$$

primary amines   secondary amines   tertiary amines

Where R again stands for a radical such as $—CH_3$ or $—C_2H_5$. The amines are basic compounds and as such are capable of forming salts with acids. Biochemically as well as chemically they form an important group.

Aromatic compounds.

The benzene nucleus is the basic unit of all the compounds belonging to this major division of organic chemicals. Benzene is a six carbon unsaturated ring compound with the formula:

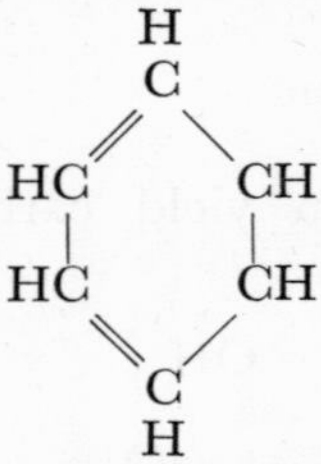

usually abbreviated as

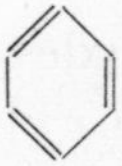

The benzene nucleus is extremely stable because it contains conjugated double bonds, i.e. alternating single and double bonds.

Aromatic compounds in general differ in properties from the types of organic substances which have been described up to this stage and which are collectively called aliphatic.

The benzene nucleus can be substituted by one or more radicals (R) such as methyl (—CH_3), hydroxyl (—OH) or carboxyl (—COOH) and with two such groups three isomers can exist:

ortho (o—)   meta (m—)   para (p—)

Thus is meta-hydroxy benzoic acid.

When there are three or more substituents it is usual to refer to their position on the ring by numbers starting with carbon atom 1 on top.   Thus

is 1:3:5 trichlorobenzene.

Aromatic acids, alcohols, amines, etc., like their aliphatic counterpart, form classes of compounds with different properties but one group—the phenols —deserve special mention.

Phenols.

Carbolic acid or phenol is a typical representative of this class which is characterized by a hydroxyl group attached directly to the aromatic nucleus.

phenol

Phenols are slightly acidic and the compound de-

picted above must be differentiated from

which is an aromatic alcohol on account of its hydroxyl group being on the side chain and not joined to a nuclear carbon atom.

This chapter on some of the fundamental aspects of chemistry should enable the reader to follow the chemical topics which appear in subsequent chapters of this book.

CHAPTER II

THE LIVING CELL

Protoplasm.

PROTOPLASM is the name given to the ground substance of living matter and this " life stuff " is the chief constituent of the muscles, brain, kidney, and other organs of the animal body and the cells of plants.

Protoplasm is not a single substance but a highly organized and variable system of substances which differs in any two living organisms or in any two parts of the same organism.

Life may be regarded as manifestations of the properties of this protoplasm. It is usually a viscous liquid though sometimes it may be gelatinous and over 75 per cent of it by weight is water. The substances in this aqueous medium may either be in true solution or else in the colloidal state, i.e. suspended in the form of very small submicroscopic particles. The stability of colloidal solutions is affected by the pH of the medium, the salt concentration and the temperature; these factors influence the stability of protoplasm to the same extent. Chemical analysis shows that the greater part of the solid constituents of protoplasm are made up from the elements carbon, hydrogen, nitrogen and oxygen, though sulphur, phosphorus and other elements are present in small quantities and are in fact essential for its functional activity. Further chemical investigation reveals that these elements are combined mainly in the form of proteins, fats and carbohydrates.

The cell.

A very simple form of life, as for example the amoeba, consists of a microscopic mass of protoplasm with a roughly spherical mass within it, the nucleus. Such a unit of living matter is called a cell and the amoeba is a unicellular organism.

The greater part of the protoplasm is composed of cytoplasm which although clear and homogeneous under the light microscope has been shown by electron microscopy* to consist of a fine network of

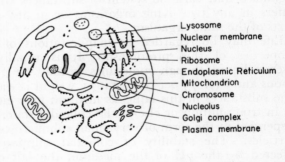

- Lysosome
- Nuclear membrane
- Nucleus
- Ribosome
- Endoplasmic Reticulum
- Mitochondrion
- Chromosome
- Nucleolus
- Golgi complex
- Plasma membrane

The internal structure of a generalized cell as visualized by the electron microscope.

canals and sac-like structures—the endoplasmic reticulum. The outer surface of this system o canals appears rough because it is covered by smal

* The electron microscope, as its name implies, uses electrons rather than light rays to visualize objects and is able to magnify parts of the cell up to 100,000 times.

granules—the ribosomes—which are involved in protein synthesis (Chap. IX).

Other important cytoplasmic components include the mitochondria which are oval or rod-like bodies with inner shelf-like structures (cristae), the lysosomes, the Golgi complex and a variety of inclusion bodies such as starch or glycogen granules (food reserves). The mitochondria act as the powerhouse of the cell, the lysosomes as an internal digestive system, while the Golgi complex appears to be associated with secretory activity.

Separated from the cytoplasm by a perforated membrane is the nucleus which is not only the main store of hereditary factors (genes) but is the centre for controlling the activities of the cytoplasm. It contains the chromosomes seen during division of the cell and also spherical masses of protoplasm distinctly separated from the rest of the nucleoplasm—the nucleoli. The latter are rich in RNA (see Chapter IX) and are also believed to be involved in the synthesis of ribosomes.

Surrounding the cell is the plasma membrane which has the important role of ensuring that only certain substances enter or leave the cell freely.

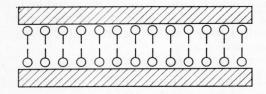

It is composed of a double layer of fatty (lipid) material, 2 molecules thick, sandwiched between a double layer of protein and is known as the " unit membrane ".

The plasma membrane is elastic and displays a high capacity for self-repair. Plant cells, in addition, possess a hard outer wall of cellulose and contain numerous disk-shaped bodies containing the green pigment-chlorophyll. These are the chloroplasts and are involved in photosynthesis.

The living cell shows the following vital activities: nutrition, growth, respiration, excretion, reproduction and irritability, i.e. the response to mechanical, thermal, chemical or electrical stimuli.

Cells usually increase in numbers by dividing into two. The nucleus divides first together with the chromosomes, and this is then followed by the cytoplasm. The process is called mitosis.

Tissues.

So far only single cells have been mentioned but all the higher forms of life are multicellular. Man himself starts life from a unicellular body, the ovum, which after fertilization divides repeatedly giving rise to all the countless millions of cells making up the body. In multicellular organisms including man each of the various parts and organs of the body is highly specialized for a particular function and the cells which form them are also modified to fulfil these roles. These aggregates of specialized cells are called tissues and the study of their structure is known as histology.

There are four main classes of tissue:

1) Epithelial tissue making up the surfaces of organs, e.g. the skin.
2) Connective tissue which includes cartilage, bone and also blood.
3) Nervous tissue.
4) Muscular tissue.

Metabolism.

Food after digestion and absorption is either oxidized to provide energy or else incorporated into the tissues which are built from it. The chemical processes involved in this and, in fact, any of the chemical reactions which occur in the living organism constitute its metabolism.

It can be considered to consist of two parts—catabolism which involves the chemical degradation of complex materials into simpler ones and anabolism which is the building up of complex substances from simpler readily available compounds. Both anabolism and catabolism proceed simultaneously in the living body but in growth and tissue repair the overall anabolism predominates while the reverse is true in certain wasting diseases. This concept of constant breakdown balanced by synthesis called a dynamic state, which goes on even in structures such as bones and teeth cannot be over-emphasized for it is essential for a full understanding of metabolism.

After death, anabolism no longer operates and there is much catabolic breakdown before bacteria and other organisms finish off the process of decomposition. This process of catabolic self-digestion after death is called autolysis.

Energy requirements.

Animals must oxidize food to provide the energy needed to do work and to maintain their tissue structures and body temperatures. Since living organisms obey the laws of thermodynamics* it is possible to account for all the energy obtained from

* Fundamental laws governing the relationship between thermal and mechanical energy.

C

food by an animal in metabolic equilibrium, i.e. with rate of tissue catabolism equal to rate of tissue anabolism. However, although in this respect living organisms can be regarded to behave like machines it would be unwise to take this analogy too far.

The total quantity of energy that it is possible to derive from a type of food, its so-called potential energy, can be found by measuring the heat produced when a given amount of it is burnt in oxygen inside a calorimeter (an apparatus used to measure quantity of heat). It is generally expressed in terms of calories; a unit that is defined as the amount of heat required to raise the temperature of one gram of water from 15°C to 16°C. However, the energy values of foodstuffs are usually given in kilocalories or Calories (1000 calories) and tables are available for most of these values.

All food is made up of three basic classes of organic compounds in different proportions. They are the carbohydrates, fats and proteins, the average calorific values of which are:

Carbohydrate: 4·2 Calories per gram
Fat   :   9·3 Calories per gram
Protein   :   5·6 Calories per gram

The first two classes are usually completely oxidized to carbon dioxide and water in the body but protein is in part excreted in the urine as urea so that its true physiological calorific value is only about 4·1 Calories per gram.

Using these figures it has been possible to show that the amount of energy derived from the combustion of food is the same whether it is burnt in a calorimeter or oxidized in several stages in the animal body.

The energy requirements of man can be determined directly by placing him inside a metal-walled, air-tight room, a sort of large calorimeter, and then measuring oxygen uptake, heat increase, amount of excreta produced etc., while on standard diet carrying out different forms of activity. In this manner it has been possible to construct tables showing the number of Calories needed for different types of activities and these are listed in order of increasing caloric requirements.

1) Sleeping.   5) Walking.
2) Lying awake.   6) Swimming.
3) Sitting.   7) Running.
4) Standing.   8) Walking upstairs.

The amount of heat produced by a subject per unit body surface area while in a state of complete rest having fasted for twelve hours beforehand is called the *basal metabolism*.

The respiratory quotient.

The respiratory quotient abbreviated R.Q. is defined as the volume of carbon dioxide evolved by the body during a given time divided by the volume of oxygen consumed and is useful in determining whether carbohydrate, fat or protein is being metabolized predominantly. In the oxidation of carbohydrate (for example, glucose) the overall equation is:

$$C_6H_{12}O_6 + 6O_2 \longrightarrow 6CO_2 + 6H_2O \qquad (1)$$
glucose

and since each gram molecule of a gas at a given temperature and pressure occupies the same volume

$$R.Q. \text{ for carbohydrate} = \frac{6CO_2}{6O_2} = 1$$

For fat it is 0·7 and for protein 0·8.

By measuring the R.Q. and the amount of nitrogenous compounds excreted it is possible to calculate the quantity of carbohydrate, fat and protein in the food eaten and thus determine indirectly the number of Calories that it provides.

Inorganic foods.

Carbohydrates, fats and proteins together with the vitamins (see Chapter X) form the organic constituents of food but the inorganic compounds such as water and the mineral salts are also of great importance.

Water.

Water is the most abundant compound in the body and it accounts for over 70 per cent of its total weight. The protoplasm of cells contains a large proportion of water as does the intercellular fluid, i.e. fluid found in between the cells, and the blood. The average intake for a human adult is about four pints of which only a little more than half is drunk as such, the rest coming from food. It may be present there as water or else formed on oxidation of carbohydrate (see equation (1) above), protein or fat. This last class of food provides twice as much metabolic water as either of the others.

The output is naturally the same as the intake—about four pints—the water being lost in the urine, faeces, sweat and in the expired air. The particular route by which water is excreted depends on the circumstances and less urine is produced in hot weather when there is excessive sweating to regulate the body temperature. Water is very important as a carrier of food to tissues and waste products away from them. It is also important as a solvent, since chemical compounds cannot influence the behaviour of living cells unless they are solution. Chemically one point of interest about water is that it is liquid when theoretically a compound with the formula H_2O should be a gas. The reason is that water is associated, i.e. a large number of molecules are held together in close association by physical forces, and really the formula should be $(H_2O)n$, where n stands for a large number.

Sodium (Na).

Usually eaten in the form of common salt (sodium chloride), it occurs within the animal mainly in the body fluids as opposed to the element potassium which is normally found inside the cells.

Sodium has a very important osmotic function: Certain membranes, among them the living cell walls are semi-permeable, i.e. they will allow the free passage of water but not of all the substances dissolved in it. When two solutions of salt, a dilute one and a more concentrated one, are separated by such a membrane, impermeable to the ions of this salt, water will be drawn from the former into the latter which consequently becomes more dilute. This phenomenon is called osmosis and the greater the concentration difference the greater will be the osmotic pressure.

Sodium ions as well as those of other elements help to maintain this osmotic pressure of the body fluids constant and thus prevent either dehydration of swelling of cells.

Two solutions which have the same osmotic pressure are called isotonic and the body cells are isotonic with a 0·9 per cent solution of sodium chloride (0·9 grams in 100 millilitres of water).

Sodium plays another important role in the body

in the form of sodium phosphate and sodium bicarbonate which act as buffers, i.e. maintain the pH of the body constant.

One of the actions of the hormones of the adrenal gland cortex (see Chapter XI) is to regulate the concentration of sodium and potassium in the body and although these elements have the same sort of metabolic role they cannot replace each other.

Phosphorus (P).

This element is present as calcium phosphate in the bones and teeth and also in organic combination with many compounds of extreme importance to the body which will be discussed in subsequent chapters.

Cheese, eggs, meat and milk are rich sources of phosphorus and as a buffer, sodium phosphate maintains acid-base equilibrium. The metabolism of phosphorus is linked with that of calcium.

Calcium (Ca).

Calcium is the other chief constituent of bone and teeth, its requirement being greatest in growing children and pregnant women. Its best food source is milk and cheese.

A fair amount of this element is found in the circulating blood plasma and it is also essential for normal blood clotting.

Vitamin D (see Chapter X) and the hormone of the parathyroid gland (see Chapter XI) have a profound effect on calcium metabolism.

Iron (Fe).

Iron is present in haemoglobin which is the red pigment responsible for the colour of blood and a dietary deficiency of this element results in anaemia.

Egg, liver and parsley are all good sources of iron, and children and pregnant women require the greatest amount of it in their diet.

It has also been found that a trace of copper is essential for haemoglobin formation which shows that an element in even minute amounts—called a trace element—can have an important biochemical role.   In all, over fifty different elements have been detected in living organisms, many of them only in traces and it is conceivable that they act like copper in other synthetic reactions.

Magnesium (Mg).

The chlorophyll of green plants is a compound chemically related to the haemoglobin of blood but contains magnesium in the place of iron.   There are also some differences in the organic part of the molecule.   Chlorophyll is required by plants for photosynthesis, i.e. the utilisation of the sun's rays to build up complex organic compounds, mainly carbohydrates, from water and the carbon dioxide in the atmosphere.

Magnesium is also essential in the animal body and symptoms of malnutrition have been shown to appear in rats kept on a diet deficient in this element.

A high concentration of magnesium in blood plasma can paralyse nerve endings, thus acting like a narcotic (sleep inducing drug).   This can be counteracted by the injection of potassium or calcium salts.

Various magnesium salts are given as laxatives and " milk of magnesia " which is a suspension of magnesium hydroxide is used as an alkaline dentifrice.   When given by mouth not much of it is absorbed by the alimentary canal and the toxic and narcotic effects are only shown when salts of this element are injected into the circulation.

Other important elements are *chlorine* from which the hydrochloric acid of the stomach is produced, *copper* which is needed for haemoglobin formation and is present in many oxidizing enzymes (see Chapter V) and iodine which is incorporated into the thyroid hormone (see Chapter XI).

CHAPTER III

EXPERIMENTAL METHODS USED IN BIOCHEMISTRY

BIOCHEMICAL experiments may be divided into two main groups. Those which are carried out on whole living animals, called " in vivo " experiments and " in vitro " ones where fresh isolated tissues such as muscle, liver or kidney, etc., are used.

Only certain kinds of animals are convenient for laboratory purposes and therefore the majority of experiments are carried out on rats, mice, guinea pigs and rabbits, all of which are relatively small with large litters. Cats, dogs and monkeys are also used and the reason for using mammals is that the results are more likely to apply to man.

In the author's experience laboratory animals are generally well fed and treated and everything done to prevent suffering during the experiments.

In all metabolic work it is essential to make allowances for species and individual differences and whenever possible a pure breed of animal should be used.

The diet, temperature and humidity of the surroundings are also important and all experiments should be repeated several times on a number of animals so as to obtain statistically significant results. (Statistics is the branch of mathematics dealing with averages and the significance of results).

"Feeding" Experiments.

This consists of giving by mouth or injecting either under the skin (subcutaneously), into a muscle (intramuscularly) or into a vein (intravenously), the compound under investigation followed by the examination of the tissues and excreta for possible degradation products.   When urine is collected for analysis a small amount of toluene (methyl benzene) is usually added to prevent any bacteria present from multiplying and attacking the compounds dissolved in it. For this reason too, urine should be stored in a refrigerator.   There is always the possibility in this type of work that some of the substances excreted have already been attacked by bacteria and therefore do not represent degradation products formed by the animal.   This is certainly true for faeces since bacteria abound in the gut of all animals.

In herbivores these microorganisms play the important role of digesting the cellulose of grass in return for food and shelter for themselves in the gut. This mutually beneficial association is called symbiosis as opposed to parasitism where organisms living inside the host are harmful to it.

By "feeding" experiments it is possible to determine what sort of chemical reactions can occur in the animal body and examples of these so called "detoxication" reactions are given below.

This term is used because generally, though not always, toxic compounds are changed to less harmful ones and excreted as such.   The metabolism of many non-toxic substances which are known to occur in the body has also been studied in experiments of this kind.

The liver and to some extent the kidneys are responsible for detoxifying foreign organic compounds and this may be achieved in several ways:

(1) Oxidation.

A large variety of compounds are oxidized in the body and most alcohols and aldehydes are converted to the corresponding acids.

Ethyl alcohol, however, is broken down completely to carbon dioxide and water and although it is produced from glucose by many plants and micro-organisms, it can be considered foreign to animals since they do not synthesize or require it.

It is of interest that antabuse, a drug used in the treatment of chronic alcoholism, inhibits the oxidation of acetaldehyde which results in the accumulation of this product in the body with disagreeable symptoms whenever alcoholic beverages are consumed.

(2) Reduction.

Though less common than oxidation, reduction of substances in the body does occur as for example:

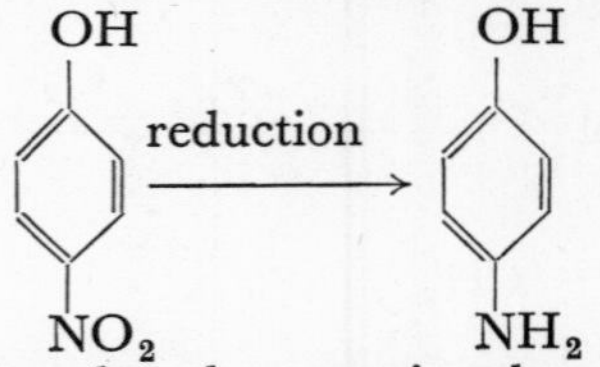

p-nitrophenol   p-aminophenol

(3) Conjugation.

The term conjugation refers to the combination of a foreign substance with a compound freely available in the body; the product formed, which is generally less toxic, is then eliminated in the urine. Conjugation often follows oxidation and in mammals benzoic acid is conjugated with the amino acid glycine (see Chapter IX) and excreted as hippuric acid.

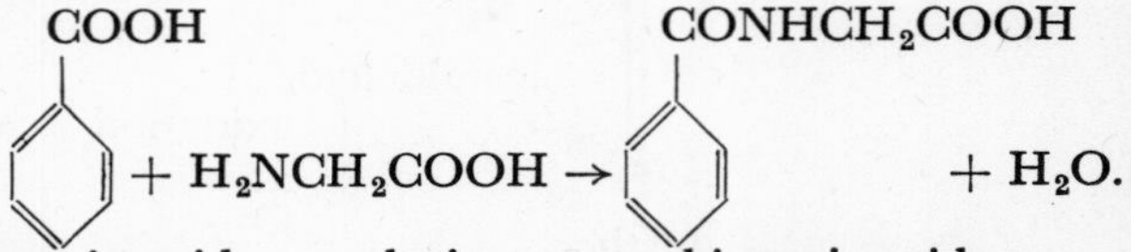

benzoic acid   glycine   hippuric acid

All substances such as toluene, benzaldehyde and benzyl alcohol which are first oxidized by benzoic acid are thus found in the urine of mammals in the form of hippuric acid. In birds however, a different amino acid—ornithine—takes the place of glycine and benzoic acid is eliminated as ornithuric acid.

Phenylacetic acid, the next homologue of benzoic acid, is conjugated with glycine in cats and dogs to form phenylaceturic acid but in man and the chimpanzee yet another amino acid—glutamine—is used for conjugation prior to elimination in the urine.

These examples show that there are several ways of detoxifying the same compound and that there are also marked differences in this respect in different groups of animals.

In mammals only part of the benzoic acid is conjugated with glycine, the rest is found combined with glucuronic acid, a substance closely allied chemically to glucose.

Phenols are also excreted as glucuronides but, in addition, they can combine with sulphate. Thus, phenol itself is excreted as sodium or potassium phenylsulphate although the glucuronide predominates when large amounts of phenol are present.

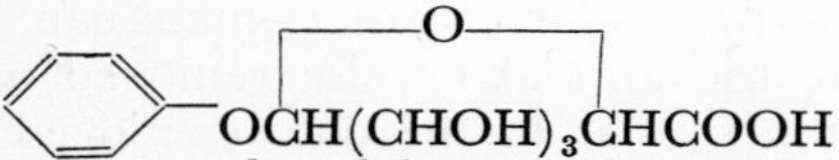

$$\text{OCH(CHOH)}_3\text{CHCOOH}$$
phenylglucuronide

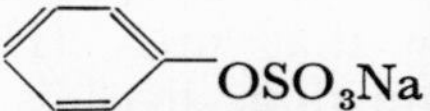

$$\text{OSO}_3\text{Na}$$
sodium phenylsulphate

Most amines are acetylated, i.e. an acetyl group (CH_3CO—) is added, and sulphanilamide which is a typical member of the sulpha drugs used against bacterial infection is eliminated as acetyl sulphanilamide.

SO$_2$NH$_2$ SO$_2$NH$_2$

acetylation   ⟶

NH$_2$ NHCOCH$_3$
sulphanilamide   acetylsulphanilamide

Many more examples showing the versatility of
the living body in detoxication could be given but
for this a more advanced textbook of biochemistry
should be consulted.

Perfusion.

The feeding experiments described above have
shown what the body as a whole can do to various
compounds but they do not indicate which particular
organs are responsible for these chemical changes.
One method of studying such changes in a specific
organ is by perfusion.

Perfusion means " passing through " and in these
experiments the substance under investigation dissolved in blood or in physiological saline*, is circu-
lated through a particular organ, which can be
either left inside the animal or else removed and
kept in a medium similar to the one it enjoyed in
the body. By this method it has been possible to
show that urea (H_2NCONH_2) is formed when
mammalian liver is perfused with a solution of
ammonium salts or that the concentration of
glucose in the blood entering the liver is higher than
the concentration of this substance in the blood

* Often called Ringer solution after the physiologist Sidney
Ringer and containing the ions of sodium, potassium, calcium,
magnesium, chloride, phosphate, sulphate and bicarbonate in fixed
concentrations at the pH of blood with which it is isotonic.

leaving it. These and other similar facts have all contributed towards giving an overall picture of metabolism.

Extirpation.

Observation of the biochemical and physiological changes that occur after surgical removal of various organs has also been adopted for studying metabolism and this method has been used extensively in the hormone field.

Valuable information can often be gained from hospital cases when, for one reason or another, a particular organ is either over-working or non-functional.

Tissue slices.

After killing the animal, the organ required is rapidly removed and extremely thin slices are cut from it and placed into warm oxygenated physiological saline. These slices will remain alive and carry out metabolic reactions for several hours.

The rate of oxygen uptake by the slices, which shows the rate at which compounds are being metabolized, can be determined by means of a Warburg manometer (pressure gauge), named after the famous German biochemist.

The tissue slices are placed into compartment B of flask F which fits on to the manometer U and is held in position by the spring A. The centre well I contains caustic potash solution (KOH) to absorb liberated carbon dioxide and a solution of the compound being tested for metabolic activity is placed into compartment C.

The joints are well greased to make them air tight and flask F is immersed in a water bath at 37°C (mammalian body temperature) after starting

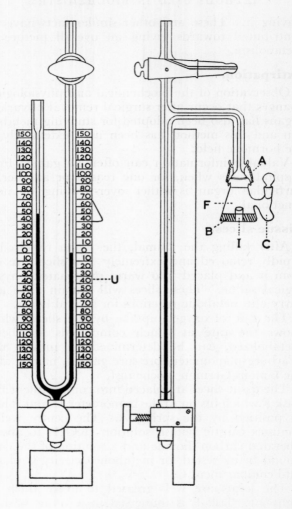

A Warburg Manometer

the experiment by tipping the contents of C into F. The whole apparatus is then gently shaken to and fro by means of a mechanical device and readings on the manometer are taken at fixed time intervals. The rate at which gases are evolved or absorbed can thus be readily determined.

The tissue slice technique is a very convenient one for studying metabolism in the laboratory, but it has the disadvantage that once the tissues are removed from the body, they no longer enjoy their normal blood supply with its essential hormones (see Chapter XI) that greatly influence many biochemical changes. Nevertheless this method has yielded much valuable information as have other " in vitro " techniques, including cell-free systems.

Homogenates.

During their metabolism, most compounds are broken down in several stages, each step being controlled by a special substance called an enzyme (see next Chapter).

Taking a hypothetical example, if a compound A is metabolized through intermediates B and C to a final degradation product D

$$A \xrightarrow{\text{enzyme 1}} B \xrightarrow{\text{enzyme 2}} C \xrightarrow{\text{enzyme 3}} D$$

then step $A \rightarrow B$ is controlled by enzyme 1, step $B \rightarrow C$ by enzyme 2, etc. In tissue slices most of the cells are intact and since there is an organized pattern of enzymes within them, each of which acts in turn, the conversion of A to D is all that is observed.

If, however, the cells are broken up this organisation is destroyed and by various techniques each enzyme can be isolated and made to work separately. Thus A would only give rise to B under the influence

D

of enzyme 1, or B only to C under the influence of enzyme 2 and so on.

A method often used is to grind up the tissue in physiological saline followed by a series of precipitations to get rid of any unwanted enzymes and cellular debris, and then to incubate the product

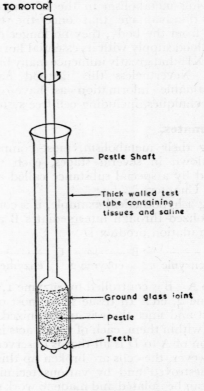

TO ROTOR

Pestle Shaft

Thick walled test tube containing tissues and saline

Ground glass joint

Pestle

Teeth

A homogenizer

with a solution of the compound under investigation.
More often, however, subcellular fractions containing
nuclei, mitochondria or the endoplasmic reticulum
(microsomes) of cells (see Chapter II) are used to
study metabolism.   They can be readily isolated by
spinning at different speeds in a centrifuge and by this
method it has been possible to show that different
groups of enzymes are localized in different cellular
components.

Several ways are known for breaking up cells to
liberate their protoplasmic constituents with their
essential enzymes.

Grinding with sand in a mortar has been used in
the past but nowadays many high speed homo-
genizers have been adopted for this purpose.   One
type in very common use consists of a thick walled
test tube in which a very close fitting mechanically
driven pestle rotates crushing the tissues between
itself and the wall of the tube.

Others have cutting blades revolving at high
speeds and even ultrasonic vibrations have been
used for this purpose.   Although many different
" in vitro " and " in vivo " methods are available
to study metabolism, no single one is capable of
giving a full picture of this process which can only
be achieved by combining the data obtained from
several different types of experiments.

Chromatography.

One of the major problems of biochemistry is
the separation of the particular compound required
for identification or estimation from the numerous
other compounds which are present in tissues or
biological fluids.   When normal methods of separation fail to remove the interfering substances, the
technique of chromatography may be applied.

The term chromatography (from the Greek: chroma-colour) originates from the time it was found that solutions of plant pigments when allowed to trickle down through a packed column of powdered alumina (Al_2O_3) or chalk $(CaCO_3)$ inside a glass cylinder gave coloured bands representing the different pigments present. A separation is thus achieved and it is then possible to cut up the extruded column and extract each coloured band with a suitable solvent.

However, the presence of colour is not essential for chromatography and compounds which are colourless but fluoresce in ultraviolet light, for example, can be treated in a similar way.

Alumina can be replaced by silica (sand), pulped paper or synthetic resins and often there is no need to cut up the column to dissolve out the required material but to allow suitable solvents to pass through and collect fractions dripping out at the bottom.

The reason that different compounds travel at different speeds is that they are adsorbed, i.e. held on to the material of the column in varying degrees and this type of separation is therefore called adsorption chromatography. The other main type which is usually carried out on strips of filter paper is known as partition chromatography and credit for this method goes to two British scientists—A. Martin and R. Synge. Both were awarded the Nobel prize for their work in this field.

In this method a solution of the material to be investigated is spotted a short way from the one end of a long rectangular strip of filter paper which is then allowed to dip into a solvent. Care is taken not to immerse the spot and as the liquid spreads over the absorbent paper it will run up or down the strip depending on whether the ascending or descending method is used.

The apparatus simply consists of a tank or jar with an air tight lid, a trough to hold liquid and the paper strip, set up as in the diagrams.

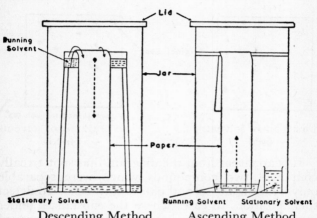

Descending Method   Ascending Method

The solvent chosen is one of a pair which does not mix such as benzene-water, the other component being used to saturate the atmosphere of the tank and the paper with its vapour. As the running solvent spreads over the paper trying to carry with it the compounds in the spot a kind of tug of war occurs between it and the other solvent (stationary phase) for the molecules in the mixture. These will travel at speeds depending on their relative solubilities in the two immiscible solvents and by choosing suitable liquid mixtures it is possible to achieve a separation.

Sometimes, however, two or more compounds travel at the same speed along the paper, resulting in overlap, but this difficulty can usually be overcome by starting with a square sheet of paper, running the solvent as before and then turning the paper through a right angle in order to repeat the process with a different pair of solvents.

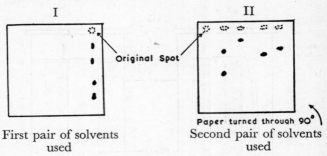

I

Original Spot

First pair of solvents used

II

Paper turned through 90°

Second pair of solvents used

It is apparent from the diagram that spot 1 really contained two compounds which were separable only by using the second pair of solvents. To detect their position, in cases where the substances under investigation are colourless the paper can be sprayed with a compound which reacts with them to give coloured products. Advantage can also be taken of any fluorescence shown by the compounds in ultra-violet light or if they absorb light of a certain wave length. Thus, by these relatively simple chromatographic techniques many biochemically important compounds have been detected and isolated from hitherto inseparable mixtures and many more are still being discovered.

Isotope experiments.

In recent times much progress has been made in biochemistry by using isotopes to solve problems of metabolism. In Chapter I it was shown that the hydrogen atom had a positive nucleus containing one proton and a single negatively charged electron revolving around it. Hydrogen however can exist in two other forms, with one or two neutrons in the nucleus. The atomic number which is the number of protons in the nucleus is still the same but the atomic weights are now different. These heavier atoms of the same element are called isotopes and, in the case of hydrogen, the one with an extra neutron is called deuterium (D) and the one with two extra neutrons, tritium (T). Some isotopes, amongst them tritium, are unstable and emit particles and rays; they are radioactive.

Isotopic atoms are normally present only in very small quantities in any element but they can be concentrated by physical and chemical methods.

To the biochemist the most important isotopes are deuterium (^{2}H) or heavy hydrogen, tritium (^{3}H) which is radioactive, ^{14}C— radioactive carbon, ^{15}N— heavy nitrogen and the heavy or radioactive forms of oxygen, phosphorus, sulphur, iodine and iron. The numeral in say ^{14}C stands for its atomic weight—normal carbon being ^{12}C. By incorporating such isotopic atoms into molecules, i.e. labelling them, it has been possible to solve many important problems of biosynthesis and breakdown. Thus it has been shown that even such complicated molecules as cholesterol (see Chapter VIII) and uric acid (see Chapter IX) are built up in the body from relatively simple compounds. ^{14}C—labelled acetic acid when fed to animals gives rise to cholesterol molecules containing atoms of this isotope and similarly ^{15}N in labelled glycine—a simple amino acid—finds its way into the molecules of uric acid.

Many other compounds also become labelled which shows the versatility of living cells in synthetic processes and by this technique it has been found that labelled fatty acids (higher homologues of acetic acid) are first deposited in the fat depots of the body before being oxidized in the liver.

Other experiments have shown that radioactive iron becomes part of the haemoglobin molecule and that radioactive iodine, like normal iodine is taken up by the thyroid gland and incorporated into thyroxine—the hormone that it produces. In addition, radioactive iodine has become a valuable agent for the diagnosis of certain thyroid disorders and also for the treatment of overactivity of this gland or thyroid cancer. Another example of isotope therapy is the use of radioactive phosphorus for the treatment of leukaemia (excess of white blood cells) and polycythaemia (excess of red blood cells). Radioactive phosphorus has also been used to determine circulatory blood volume, and radioactive iron to measure the normal life span of red blood cells in health and disease.

Numerous other problems of nutrition, photosynthesis, antigen-antibody interaction and membrane permeability, to mention but a few examples, have been solved by this extremely valuable modern technique.

CHAPTER IV

BIOCHEMICAL CATALYSIS

The Enzymes.

IT is a remarkable fact that complex chemical synthetic and breakdown reactions are carried out much more rapidly and easily by the living organism at body temperature than is possible in the laboratory even under drastic conditions. In fact many biologically occurring compounds have never been made artificially.

The reason is that these reactions are aided by catalysts which occur in all living matter, namely, enzymes. A catalyst is a compound which accelerates chemical reaction but yet remains unchanged at the end of the process although its physical appearance may alter. The platinum gauze catalyst used in the industrial oxidation of ammonia shows considerable roughening after some weeks of use but it is still the same substance—unchanged platinum—after all that time. Since a catalyst enters into a reaction without itself being used up, a very small amount of it can usually bring about considerable chemical change. Thus minute quantities of finely divided (colloidal) platinum can catalyze the decomposition of enormous amounts of hydrogen peroxide.

$$2H_2O_2 \xrightarrow[\text{catalyst}]{\text{platinum}} 2H_2O + O_2$$

Most catalytic processes are surface reactions which explains why finely divided materials with a larger surface area are generally the most efficient catalysts. This is borne out by the fact that smooth sheets of platinum do not cause liberation of oxygen from hydrogen peroxide.

Water too can act as a catalyst. Perfectly dry hydrogen and chlorine will not react to form hydrochloric acid and dry carbon will not burn in moisture-free oxygen.

Finally, catalysts do not affect the equilibrium position of reversible reactions since they increase the speed of both forward and reverse reactions equally.

Enzymes (from the Greek—in yeast) are complex organic catalysts, produced by living cells, which possess a high degree of selection (specificity) towards the substances on which they act.

Although the effects of biological catalysts have been known and utilized by mankind since early times for the production of cheese and alcoholic beverages, and their role in digestion had been demonstrated by Spallanzani in the 18th century, our present knowledge has evolved mainly from the work of Pasteur. He showed that a solution of sugar was perfectly stable and would keep almost indefinitely if sterilized and kept in airtight jars but would readily produce alcohol and carbon dioxide, i.e. ferment, if living yeast cells were allowed to contaminate it. Similarly, the souring of wines and milk could be attributed to other microorganisms. However, it was Buchner in 1897 who showed that cell-free extracts of yeast were still able to ferment sugars and that although enzymes are produced only by living cells, they are independent of them for their activities. The substance upon which an enzyme acts is known as the substrate and it is customary to name enzymes after their substrates by adding the suffix—*ase*. Thus, urease acts on urea and amylase

on starch (Latin—amylum). Often enzymes are
called after the type of reaction they catalyze, as
for example, succinic dehydrogenase. Here, the
function of the enzyme, i.e. the removal of hydrogen
(dehydrogenation or oxidation) as well as the nature
of the substrate is described. In some cases,
however, the older nomenclature has persisted and
the original names for many of the digestive enzymes
such as pepsin, trypsin and rennin are still in current
use.

Properties of enzymes.

Even before 1926, when James Sumner first
succeeded in isolating the enzyme urease in pure
crystalline form there had been a considerable mass
of evidence to indicate that these biological catalysts
were proteins. This type of compound (Chapter
IX) is made up of many different amino acids and
generally has a very high molecular weight. Because of their complex three-dimensional structures,
the properties of proteins are easily altered by gentle
heating, changes of pH, dehydration (removal of
the water layer surrounding the molecule), and even
violent shaking. The sort of change that takes
place is called denaturation and is very much like
the one that occurs to egg white when an egg is
boiled. Enzymes therefore are also profoundly
affected by all these factors but before going any
further one important and striking property that
they possess—namely their specificity—must be
discussed.

Specificity.

Most enzymes can only catalyze a limited number
of reactions and are extremely particular about the
structure of the compounds on which they act—they

are in fact specific. Thus, urease brings about the hydrolysis of urea (H_2NCONH_2) but is without action on methyl urea ($H_2NCONHCH_3$), and arginase acts only on the amino acid, arginine, but on none of its derivatives. Other examples are succinic dehydrogenase which helps to oxidize succinic acid to fumaric acid (see Chapter VII), and the maltase found in germinating barley (malt) which brings about the conversion of the sugar maltose to glucose.

Another type of extreme specificity is shown by the lactic dehydrogenase of muscle which catalyzes the oxidation of only one of the two optically active forms (see Chapter VI) of lactic acid.

Many enzymes, however, are less exacting about the structure of their substrates and, for example, maltase from the intestinal juice of mammals attacks not only maltose (glucose-α-glucoside) but also many other sugars that contain an α-linked glucose unit. Maltase from mammalian sources therefore differs from the highly specific enzyme in malt and is more accurately called α-glucosidase.

Enzymes with very low specificity are uncommon and the protein-digesting enzymes pepsin and trypsin which were formerly believed to be able to hydrolyze any molecule with a peptide linkage such as R—CO—NH—R' are now known to be more selective and dependent on the nature of both R and R' which represent amino acids. It has been found that many enzymes with low specificity are, in fact, mixtures of components with more stringent structural requirements.

The effect of temperature.

The speed of chemical reactions increases with increasing temperature and this is also true for reactions catalyzed by enzymes. However, since these biocatalysts are rather susceptible to even gentle heating and lose their catalytic activities on denaturation it follows that for each enzyme catalyzed reaction there is an optimum tempera- ture. Below it, the enzyme is stable but the rate of reaction is small and above it, though the rate is high, the reaction is rather shortlived because the enzyme is destroyed.

The effect of pH.

Enzymes are also very sensitive to changes in acidity and are active as catalysts only over a very limited pH range on either side of their optimum pH. This value generally lies near that of the environment in which the enzyme performs its catalytic function and is therefore close to neutrality (pH 7). However, it may be very much on the acid side for an enzyme such as pepsin which helps to digest protein in the stomach.

Most enzymes rapidly lose their activity if condi- tions are made too acid or alkaline.

Mode of action of enzymes.

The simplest way to represent enzyme action is by the so-called " lock and key " mechanism. Before either molecule A—B can decompose to A and B or combination occur, A—B, or A and B, must be adsorbed, in close proximity to each other, on to the surface of the enzyme. This can only happen when the shape of the surface is just right (specific) for a given compound and the projecting parts in the diagram represent reactive chemical groups in the substrate and enzyme.

Many catalytic poisons (inhibitors) act by settling

on to the active parts of the surface of the enzyme
and thereby prevent the substrate from reaching it.

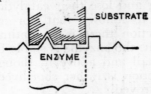

active part of surface

Diagramatic representation of enzyme—substrate
interaction.

Competitive inhibition.

It is also possible to explain competitive inhibition
by the " lock and key " hypothesis.   If $A \xrightarrow{\text{enzyme}} X$
then a competitive inhibitor is a compound B which
resembles A structurally and combines with the
enzyme but does not give rise to X.   This means
that compounds A and B are in competition for a
place on the enzyme with the result that less X is
formed.

The amount of inhibition will depend on the
amount of B present.   Thus the rate of oxidation of
succinic acid by succinic dehydrogenase is reduced
if malonic acid is added and this decrease is pro-
portional to the amount of inhibitor.

$$
\begin{array}{ll}
\text{CH}_2\text{COOH} & \text{CH}_2\text{COOH} \\
| & | \\
\text{CH}_2\text{COOH} & \text{COOH} \\
\text{succinic acid} & \text{malonic acid}
\end{array}
$$

The recognition that an enzyme may be inhibited
by compounds posssesing a structure closely related
to that of the normal substrate has found wide
application in biology and medicine.   The anti-

bacterial drug sulphanilamide acts by inhibiting competitively the utilization of para aminobenzoic acid (PAB) which is indispensable for the growth of many bacteria but is not required by man.

$$H_2N— \bigcirc —COOH \qquad H_2N— \bigcirc —SO_2NH_2$$

para aminobenzoic acid
(PAB)
sulphanilamide

PAB is essential to bacteria for the synthesis of folic acid whereas man and other mammals cannot synthesize folic acid and must obtain this vital compound preformed in the diet.

In both these examples of competitive inhibition there is a striking resemblance in structure between the active and inhibiting molecules.

The antibiotic penicillin interferes with the synthesis of specific substances needed for the formation of the cell wall in certain groups of bacteria. Since mammalian cells do not possess such a cell wall, it is evident why penicillin is harmless to man and only influences bacterial metabolism.

Enzyme induction.

Bacteria, however, may become resistant to penicillin by developing the enzyme penicillinase which breaks down this antibiotic and, similarly, other microorganisms can acquire this ability to metabolize substances when grown in their presence.

This adaptive phenomenon, known as enzyme induction, which results in the formation of increased amounts of the appropriate enzyme has also been observed in mammals. Thus, the activity of an enzyme that oxidizes tryptophan, tryptophan pyrrolase, can be greatly increased by administering

this amino acid to animals and appears to be determined by its concentration in the blood.

In general, substrates stimulate the formation of
the corresponding enzymes whereas the products
decrease their synthesis, and this provides a mechanism for the control of biochemical reactions.

Coenzymes.

Many enzymes are unable to act as catalysts
unless certain activators or coenzymes are present.
These may be:

a) inorganic ions such as those of magnesium,
zinc, or manganese which help to bring substrate and enzyme in closer union together.

b) organic reducing agents such as ascorbic
acid (vitamin C) and glutathione (see Chapter
X) which help to maintain —SH (sulphydryl)
groups of enzymes in the reduced state.
Many enzymes lose their catalytic activities
when these groups become oxidized.

c) Complex organic compounds such as thiamine
pyrophosphate and nicotinamide adenine dinucleotide (NAD). The former which is the

$$R-S\!-\!H \quad H\!-\!S-R \;\rightleftharpoons\; R-S-S-R + H_2O$$

glutathione or ascorbic acid

pyrophosphate of vitamin B_1 (thiamine) is
also called cocarboxylase because it is the
coenzyme for carboxylase. This enzyme catalyzes the liberation of carbon dioxide from
keto acids such as pyruvic acid.

$$\begin{array}{ccc} CH_3 & & CH_3 \\ | & \xrightarrow[\text{carboxylase}]{\text{carboxylase}} & | \quad + \ CO_2 \\ CO & & CHO \\ | & & \text{acetaldehyde} \\ COOH & & \end{array}$$
pyruvic acid

The latter compound NAD which is also known as coenzyme I or DPN is involved in many oxidative processes where it acts as a hydrogen acceptor and coenzyme to dehydrogenating enzymes (see Chapters V and VII).

d) Enzymes which will convert inactive " pro-enzymes " or " zymogens " into active enzymes. Thus, the pancreatic juice contains two pro-enzymes, chymotrypsinogen and trypsinogen which will attack protein only when they are changed to chymotrypsin and trypsin respectively. This is achieved for the latter compound by enterokinase, present in intestinal juice, and the trypsin that is formed then activates not only chymotrypsinogen but also its own proenzyme (autocatalysis).

$$\text{trypsinogen} \xrightarrow{\text{enterokinase}} \text{trypsin}$$

$$\left.\begin{array}{l} \text{chymotrypsinogen} \\ \text{trypsinogen} \end{array}\right\} \xrightarrow{\text{trypsin}} \begin{array}{l} \text{chymotrypsin} \\ \text{trypsin.} \end{array}$$

Chymotrypsin, however, has no action on either trypsinogen or its own zymogen.

The pepsin of gastric juice is also liberated in an inactive form and is activated by the hydrochloric acid of the stomach and by autocatalysis.

Activation of this kind has often been called " unmasking " because the activating agent acts by removing a " mask " covering the active surface of the enzyme.

E

Classification of enzymes.

There are many different types of enzymes which may be arbitrarily divided into the following groups on the basis of the reactions they catalyze:

1) *Hydrolytic enzymes.*

These enzymes catalyze the splitting of their respective substrates by water (hydrolysis).

$$R—R + H—OH \rightarrow R—OH + RH$$

The main digestive enzymes belong to this class and include:

a) *Peptidases*: Proteolytic (protein-splitting) enzymes such as pepsin of gastric juice, trypsin and chymotrypsin of pancreatic juice and the amino-, carboxy- and dipeptidases of intestinal secretion.

b) *Carbohydrases*: Enzymes which attack sugars or more complex carbohydrates such as starch and glycogen. They catalyze the hydrolysis of glycosidic linkages (see Chapter VI).

c) *Esterases*: Enzymes such as the lipases which break down fats into fatty acids and glycerol, and the phosphatases and sulphatases which split esters of sulphuric and phosphoric acid respectively. Another esterase, ribonuclease, catalyzes the hydrolysis of RNA (see Chapter IX), and the full sequence of the 124 amino acids constituting this enzyme has now been determined.

In addition to the enzymes that fall into these three sections, a number of individual ones are known such as arginase which acts on the amino acid arginine and urease which breaks down urea to carbon dioxide and ammonia.

$$H_2N-CO-NH_2 + H_2O \xrightarrow{\text{urease}} CO_2 + 2NH_3$$
urea

Urease is found in many plant tissues but never in the higher animals because ammonia is very toxic to them.

2) *Oxidizing enzymes.* (See Chapter V.)

The enzymes in this class catalyze oxidative processes. They include the dehydrogenases, peroxidase, catalase, phenol and polyphenol oxidase, cytochrome oxidase and luciferase, which is present in the firefly and which acts on luciferin to produce light (bioluminescence).

3) *Adding enzymes.*

These enzymes catalyze the addition of water, ammonia, carbon dioxide or complex organic molecules and also their removal since most of these reactions are reversible.

Thus, fumarase catalyzes the interconversion of malic and fumaric acid with the addition or removal of water, while aspartase catalyzes a similar reaction involving ammonia.

$$
\begin{array}{ccccc}
\text{COOH} & & \text{COOH} & & \text{COOH} \\
| & +NH_3 & | & +H_2O & | \\
\text{CHNH}_2 & \xleftarrow{\hspace{0.5cm}} & \text{CH} & \xrightarrow{\hspace{0.5cm}} & \text{CHOH} \\
| & \text{aspartase} & \| & \text{fumarase} & | \\
\text{CH}_2 & \xrightarrow{\hspace{0.5cm}} & \text{CH} & \xleftarrow{\hspace{0.5cm}} & \text{CH}_2 \\
| & -NH_3 & | & -H_2O & | \\
\text{COOH} & & \text{COOH} & & \text{COOH} \\
\text{aspartic} & & \text{fumaric} & & \text{malic} \\
\text{acid} & & \text{acid} & & \text{acid}
\end{array}
$$

Carboxylase, which has already been mentioned in this chapter, liberates carbon dioxide from pyruvic acid but this reaction is believed to be irreversible.

Other examples include the zinc-containing enzyme, carbonic anhydrase, which is involved in the formation and breakdown of carbonic acid (H_2CO_3), and aldolase which helps to split a 6-carbon atom sugar (fructose diphosphate) into two 3-carbon atom compounds (triose phosphate).

4) *Transferring enzymes.*

These enzymes catalyze the exchange of whole sections of the molecule between two substrates and many examples of such reactions are known in biochemistry. Thus, in transmethylation, a methyl group is transferred from one molecule to another while in transphosphorylation, a phosphate group is involved. In a similar type of reaction, known as transamination, a specific enzyme catalyzes the interconversion of an amino and a keto acid.

$$
\begin{array}{ccc}
CH_3 & COOH & \\
| & | & \\
CHNH_2 + CH_2 & \xrightarrow{} & C=O \\
| & | & \\
COOH & C=O & COOH \\
& | & \\
& COOH &
\end{array}
$$

transaminase

alanine   oxaloacetic acid   pyruvic acid   aspartic acid
(amino acid) (keto acid)   (keto acid)   (amino acid)

Several other types of enzymic reactions are known and isomerases, for example, catalyze the rearrangement of atoms within their substrates while mutases are involved in the shift of a group from one position in the molecule to another. The biochemical importance of many of the individual enzymes classified above will be considered in subsequent chapters.

CHAPTER V

BLOOD AND BIOLOGICAL OXIDATION

THE digestion of food by the enzymes of the alimentary tract and their absorption are merely the first steps towards a more fundamental process—namely cellular oxidation. It is in this manner by a chain of reactions ultimately involving molecular oxygen that most of the energy present in food is liberated and utilized by the body for synthetic and other reactions.

Oxygen which makes up one fifth of the total volume of air is taken up by the blood in the capillaries of the lungs and is transported from there to all parts of the body. The lungs are also responsible for the release and expulsion of most of the carbon dioxide formed during oxidation of food.

As mentioned earlier (see Chapter II) the respiratory quotient is dependent on the nature of the food being burnt in the body.

Blood.

Blood is the fluid which carries food and oxygen to all parts of the body and also removes the waste products which are to be excreted, away from their site of formation. It is composed of cells or corpuscles floating in the plasma, a clear, slightly alkaline (pH 7·4) pale yellow fluid containing dissolved proteins and metabolic products.

One of these proteins, fibrinogen, forms a meshwork of threads (blood clots) sealing up wounds when it is converted to fibrin by the enzyme, thrombin. This process which is very much more complicated than indicated here is described in greater detail in Chapter IX.

Serum is plasma from which fibrinogen has been removed and one way of achieving this is to whip freshly drawn blood with a rod to make the fibrin adhere to it. Such defibrinated blood cannot coagulate and is generally used in laboratory experiments.

Blood consists of three main types of cells: red corpuscles (erythrocytes) which carry oxygen, white corpuscles (leucocytes) which have a protective role, killing invading bacteria, and platelets which assist in blood clotting.

Haemoglobin.

The red blood corpuscles owe their colour* to the haemoglobin they contain and mammalian life could not exist in the absence of this respiratory pigment. The solubility of oxygen in water is so low that blood without haemoglobin could only carry about 1/60th of its normal load of oxygen and would therefore have to circulate sixty times faster to keep the tissues adequately supplied with this gas—a clearly impossible task.

In vertebrates (animals with backbones), haemoglobin is found inside the corpuscles but in some invertebrates this respiratory pigment is in solution in the plasma and tissue fluids.

Haemoglobin acts by combining with oxygen when this gas is readily available, as in the lungs and releasing it again when there is a lack of oxygen. It consists of a complex organic molecule containing an iron atom in the reduced ferrous state (Fe^{++})—

* Oxyhaemoglobin is bright red in colour and haemoglobin, its reduced form, is purple.

haem, attached to a protein molecule—globin. Hence the name haemoglobin. The non-protein component of such molecules is known as a prosthetic group.

Chlorophyll, the green pigment of plants has a structure which is rather similar but magnesium replaces iron.

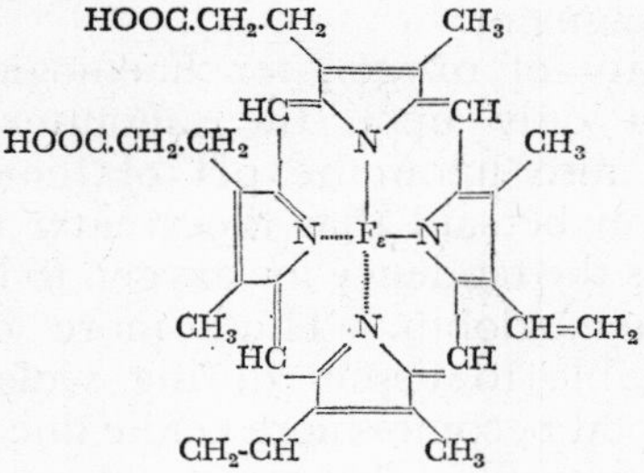

Haem

When oxygen combines with haem it does not oxidize the ferrous form of the iron (Fe^{++}) to ferric (Fe^{+++}) but merely adds itself on to the molecule. This reversible process is an oxygenation and not a true oxidation.

$$Hb + O_2 \rightleftharpoons HbO_2$$
haemoglobin   oxyhaemoglobin

Haem itself does not possess the property of a respiratory pigment which is conferred to it by the protein (globin) part of the molecule.

Haemoglobin can react with gases other than oxygen and has a very much greater affinity for carbon monoxide. This explains why car exhaust fumes which contain this gas are so dangerous and in carbon monoxide poisoning death is essentially due to lack of oxygen. The brilliant cherry-red colour of carboxyhaemoglobin is very distinctive.

Strictly speaking haemoglobin is a group of compounds because each type of animal has its own variety of globin. Thus human haemoglobin differs from that of the rat or the camel or the worm. If other proteins are substituted for globin or if the latter is denatured, or if the ferrous iron atom is oxidized to the ferric state as in methaemoglobin, the resulting compound can no longer act as a respiratory pigment.

The affinity of oxygen for haemoglobin is dependent not only upon the amount of the gas present but also upon the pH of the blood. In general it can be said that the greater the acidity, the greater is the tendency for oxygen to be liberated from oxyhaemoglobin. Thus, more oxygen becomes available to tissues during violent exercise when the blood becomes more acidic due to accumulation of lactic acid.

Human red blood corpuscles contain at least two kinds of haemoglobin, a foetal and an adult type. Foetal haemoglobin has a high affinity for oxygen which is undoubtedly of value to the foetus during its development in the uterus. It is completely replaced by adult haemoglobin within about six months of birth.

A count of the number of red corpuscles, which usually also represents the amount of haemoglobin present, has shown that the unborn child has more of this respiratory pigment than the adult and that a sex-difference exists with men having more than women. At high altitudes the blood count increases to compensate for the subnormal amount of oxygen in the atmosphere.

Methaemoglobinaemia.

It has already been mentioned that when the ferrous iron atom of haemoglobin is oxidized to the ferric state, the resulting methaemoglobin has no

activity as an oxygen carrier. Traces of methaemoglobin are normally present in blood but in some
infections or after the administration of large amounts
of certain drugs, this oxidation product of haemoglobin may appear in quantity in the blood and
urine; a condition known as methaemoglobinaemia.
In all such cases, the symptoms are similar to those
resulting from a lack of oxygen and if over 60 per
cent of the blood haemoglobin is converted to
methaemoglobin the condition becomes fatal. Methaemoglobin, however, can be reconverted rapidly
to its active form, haemoglobin, by the administration of reducing agents such as ascorbic acid (vitamin
C) and the body itself will do this to a limited extent.

There is another type of methaemoglobinaemia
which occurs more in certain families than in the
general population and is therefore an inherited
condition. A fairly high level (20–40 per cent) of
methaemoglobin is constantly present in the blood
of these individuals who lack a certain inheritable
factor needed for the reduction of methaemoglobin.
This condition is not serious but very inconvenient
since any violent exercise requiring much oxygen is
impossible. Reducing agents only have a temporary
beneficial effect in the inherited form of this disease.

The metabolism of haemoglobin.

Although even a compound as complex as haemoglobin is built up in the body from relatively simple
components certain special substances must also be
present before this can be achieved. These include
iron, a trace of copper, folic acid and vitamin B_{12},
a substance containing the element cobalt. Vitamin
B_{12} is also known as the antipernicious anaemia
factor and was not isolated in crystalline form until
1948.

The main site of haemoglobin synthesis is the bone marrow and it is broken down chiefly by the spleen into the bile pigments, bilirubin and biliverdin. They are responsible for the greenish colour of bile and prior to excretion they are converted to stercobilin responsible for the brown colour of faeces, and to urochrome, the chief pigment of urine.

In jaundice which is either caused by obstruction of bile flow or excessive destruction of haemoglobin, bile or bile pigments get into the general circulation and are deposited in the skin, giving it a characteristic yellow colour.

Biological oxidation.

The majority of the compounds which are metabolised in the tissues cannot be oxidized directly by oxygen released from oxyhaemoglobin and certain enzymes and coenzymes must be present before this can occur.

In the living cell most oxidations are brought about by the removal of hydrogen (dehydrogenation) and a simple laboratory example of such a reaction is the catalytic conversion of acetaldehyde to acetic acid by finely divided palladium (Pd). The reaction proceeds as follows:

acetaldehyde   acetaldehyde   acetic
                      hydrate   acid

The reaction involves the addition of water with subsequent removal of hydrogen so that overall oxygen has been added to the acetaldehyde molecule.

Under certain circumstances, the reduced form of palladium can pass on its hydrogen atoms to another reducible molecule—say M—with the result that acetaldehyde is oxidized to acetic acid at the expense of M being reduced to M H_2.

b) $M + Pd. 2H \longrightarrow M H_2 + Pd$

The palladium has thus remained unchanged but has acted as an intermediate carrier of hydrogen.

In the animal body such carriers are organic compounds and several of them may act in sequence. Thus, if a molecule AH_2 is oxidized to A at the expense of B, and if X and Y are intermediate carriers, the process can be represented by:

1) $AH_2 + X \xrightarrow{\text{enzyme 1}} A + XH_2$

2) $XH_2 + Y \xrightarrow{\text{enzyme 2}} X + YH_2$

3) $YH_2 + B \xrightarrow{\text{enzyme 3}} Y + BH_2$

overall change $AH_2 + B \longrightarrow A + BH_2$

Now if B happens to be oxygen then it has managed to convert AH_2 to A and water by means of the intermediate carriers, and the appropriate enzymes. The latter are collectively known as dehydrogenases if they catalyze the removal of hydrogen as in reactions 1) and 2) above and oxidases if they catalyze the addition of oxygen as in reaction 3), in which B stands for oxygen.

The intermediate carriers X and Y act as co-enzymes to the dehydrogenases and oxidases.

The oxidation of lactic acid, formed from glycogen in muscles during strenuous activity, is a good example of the type of reaction just described. The overall change is:

$$
\begin{array}{ccc}
\underset{\substack{|\\ \text{CHOH}\\ |\\ \text{COOH}}}{\text{CH}_3} + \frac{1}{2}\text{O}_2 \longrightarrow & \underset{\substack{|\\ \text{CO}\\ |\\ \text{COOH}}}{\text{CH}_3} + \text{H}_2\text{O}
\end{array}
$$

lactic acid pyruvic acid

but in actual fact the oxidation is stepwise and occurs as follows:

1)

$$
\underset{\substack{|\\ \text{CHOH} + \text{NAD}\\ |\\ \text{COOH}}}{\text{CH}_3} \xrightarrow[\text{dehydrogenase}]{\text{lactic}} \underset{\substack{|\\ \text{CO} + \text{NADH}_2\\ |\\ \text{COOH}}}{\text{CH}_3}
$$

2)

$$
\text{NADH}_2 + \text{cytochrome} \xrightarrow[\text{enzyme}]{\text{flavoprotein}} \text{NAD} + \text{reduced cytochrome}
$$

3)

$$
\text{Reduced cytochrome} + \text{O}_2 \xrightarrow[\text{oxidase}]{\text{cytochrome}} \text{cytochrome} + \text{H}_2\text{O}
$$

If reduced NAD were not reoxidized by cytochrome then reaction 1) would stop as soon as all the available coenzyme had been reduced and it would no longer act catalytically.

The reaction would similarly soon come to a halt were not the reduced cytochrome reoxidized by oxygen in the presence of cytochrome oxidase.

In certain cases, however, NAD is not essential and the hydrogen atoms removed from the substrate are added directly on to cytochrome. The biological oxidation of succinic acid by succinic dehydrogenase falls into this category.

$$
\underset{\substack{|\\ \text{CH}_2\text{COOH}}}{\text{CH}_2\text{COOH}} \xrightarrow[\text{cytochrome} + \text{oxygen}]{\text{succinic dehydrogenase}} \underset{\substack{\|\\ \text{CHCOOH}}}{\text{CHCOOH}} + \text{H}_2\text{O}
$$

succinic acid fumaric acid

This sequence of oxidative reactions is very much more complex than has been described and the enzymes involved have been shown to be arranged in an organized manner within the mitochondria (see Chapter II) of the cells. During the stepwise transfer of hydrogen from substrate to oxygen by the enzymes of this "respiratory chain", energy is trapped in the form of ATP (see Chapter VII) and it is by this process that living organisms obtain most of the energy that they require.

A fuller account of certain individual carriers of the respiratory chain will now be given.

Nicotinamide coenzymes.

Two very important intermediate carriers of hydrogen, NAD and NADP, are present in virtually all living tissues and have been isolated from yeast and also from blood, muscle, liver and many other sources. Both are composed of nicotinamide (the amide of nicotinic acid—see Chapter X), the sugar ribose (see Chapter VI), adenine (see Chapter IX) and phosphoric acid linked as:

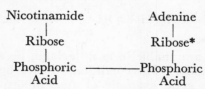

Nicotinamide   Adenine
    | |
  Ribose   Ribose*
    | |
Phosphoric ——————— Phosphoric
   Acid   Acid

Nicotinamide adenine dinucleotide (NAD)
(NADP contains an extra phosphate group at *)

Nicotinic acid, a member of the vitamin B complex (see Chapter X), is readily incorporated into NAD and NADP and consequently a deficiency of it in the diet results in decreased synthesis of these vital coenzymes needed for the normal metabolism of food constituents.

Cytochromes.

Other important carriers of the respiratory chain are the cytochromes which resemble haemoglobin chemically in that they are made up of an iron-containing haem prosthetic group attached to protein.

They occur in microorganisms as well as in animal tissues and although cytochrome c is the best known representative of this group, it is generally found together with cytochrome b and cytochrome oxidase.

Oxidases.

These enzymes catalyze the oxidation of various compounds even in the absence of intermediate carriers, by utilizing molecular oxygen as hydrogen acceptor. Such an enzyme is tyrosinase which is involved in the oxidation of the amino acid tyrosine to melanin, the brown pigment of hair and skin.

$$HO-\langle\ \rangle-CH_2CHCOOH \xrightarrow[\text{tyrosinase}]{O_2} melanin$$

$$\overset{\displaystyle NH_2}{|}$$

tyrosine

Albinos are unable to form melanin because they lack tyrosinase. This condition, which is hereditary, provides a good example of an " inborn error of metabolism ".

Tyrosinase is a copper-containing protein and is found in many plants as well as in the squid whose black " ink " consists of melanin. They liberate this dark pigment to escape from their enemies.

Ascorbic acid oxidase is also a copper-containing enzyme present in plants and it catalyzes the oxidation of ascorbic acid (Vitamin C) to dehydro-ascorbic acid.

Cytochrome oxidase, as already mentioned, is an iron-containing protein of universal distribution which oxidizes reduced cytochrome.

Other oxidases include *polyphenol oxidase* responsible for the browning of the cut surfaces of apples and potatoes, *amino acid oxidase* and *xanthine oxidase* (see Chapter X).

In many cases, oxidases catalyze reactions in which hydrogen peroxide (H_2O_2) instead of water is formed:

$$a) \quad AH_2 \xrightarrow[\text{oxidase}]{\frac{1}{2}O_2} A + H_2O$$

$$b) \quad AH_2 \xrightarrow[\text{oxidase}]{O_2} A + H_2O_2$$

Hydrogen peroxide, however, is never found free in either plant or animal tissues because two very efficient enzymes—peroxidase which occurs mainly in plants, and catalase, decompose this substance.

$$2H_2O_2 \xrightarrow[\text{or peroxidase}]{\text{catalase}} 2H_2O + O_2$$

CHAPTER VI

THE CARBOHYDRATES

THE carbohydrates are one of the major constituents of living matter and their main function is to act as a source of energy although in plants they may also have a structural role. They consist of either low molecular weight compounds with a sweet taste, the sugars, or of more complex substances such as glycogen, starch and cellulose. They all contain the elements carbon, hydrogen and oxygen and they were originally called carbohydrates because their general formula $C_x(H_2O)_y$,* is that of a hydrate of carbon.

The carbohydrates are all aldehyde or ketone alcohols and most of the biologically important members of this group are composed of units containing five or six carbon atoms (pentoses and hexoses) or multiples of these.

The carbohydrates may be classified as follows:

1) Monosaccharides.

        a) Pentoses $C_5H_{10}O_5$ Eg. Ribose

        b) Hexoses $C_6H_{12}O_6$ Eg. Glucose

2) Disaccharides $C_{12}H_{22}O_{11}$ Eg. Sucrose

3) Polysaccharides $(C_6H_{10}O_5)_x$ Eg. Starch

The monosaccharides.

Glucose. Often called grape sugar because of its occurrence in ripe grapes, glucose is also found in other plants, in blood and in the urine of untreated diabetics. It is also the unit building block for

---

* x and y stand for whole numbers which can vary for different carbohydrates.

many of the complex carbohydrates such as glycogen and starch and these polysaccharides yield glucose on acid hydrolysis.

Glucose is classified as a hexose sugar because it contains six carbon atoms and it possesses a cyclic structure, derived from the open-chain form in the following manner:

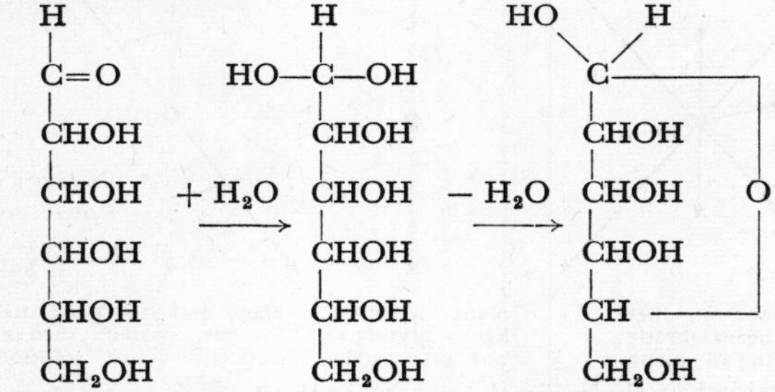

| open chain form | glucose hydrate | ring form |

The ring form can also be written as:

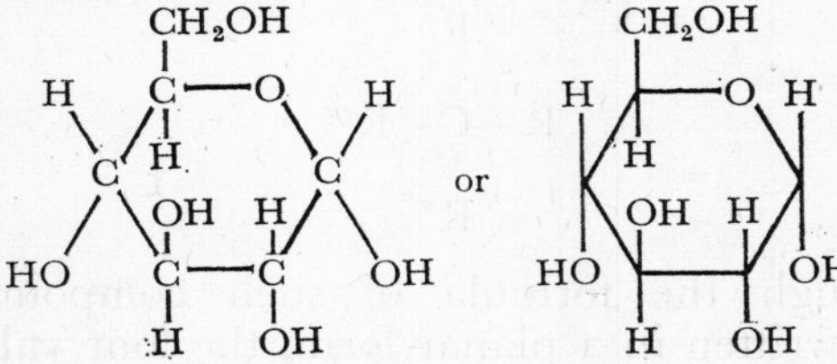

or

Sugars with six-membered rings containing an oxygen atom are said to have a pyranose structure.

Glucose is a white crystalline solid, readily soluble in water, which in sweetness is only surpassed by two other sugars, namely fructose and sucrose.

Optical activity.

The sugars, including glucose and many other naturally occurring compounds, have the remarkable

F

property of being able to rotate the plane of polarized light (i.e. light vibrating in one plane only) either to the left or to the right. They are optically active and are said to be dextrorotatory if they rotate the plane of polarized light to the right and laevorotatory if they rotate it in the opposite direction.

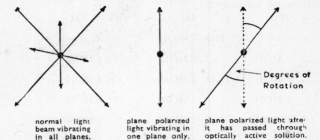

normal light beam vibrating in all planes.

plane polarized light vibrating in one plane only.

plane polarized light after it has passed through optically active solution.

Optical activity is shown by all organic compounds that contain at least one asymmetric carbon atom bearing four different elements or groups.

$$R—\overset{\displaystyle R'}{\underset{\displaystyle R''}{C}}—R'''$$

Although the formula of such compounds is usually written in a planar form, the four valencies of the carbon atom are in reality directed towards the corners of a regular tetrahedron (see Chapter I). A compound containing an asymmetric carbon atom can exist in both dextrorotatory $(+)$ and laevorotatory $(-)$ forms, one being the mirror image of the other, but in nature only one of these is generally present. However, if the compound in question is synthesized in the laboratory, both types are formed in equal quantities and no optical rotation can be observed. Such a mixture of the $(+)$ and $(-)$ forms is called a racemic mixture.

Glucose occurs naturally only in the $(+)$ form which explains why it is also known as dextrose.

In the ring structure, glucose and other sugars can exist in yet two other forms (α- and β-) which are interconvertible in solution with a change in optical rotation (mutarotation). Thus, there are two $(+)$ forms and two $(-)$ forms of glucose depending on the position of H and OH on carbon atom number 1.

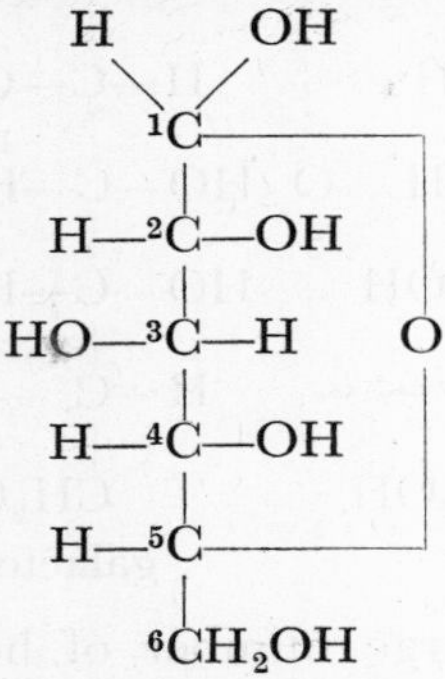

$\alpha\ (+)$ glucose $\alpha\ (-)$ glucose

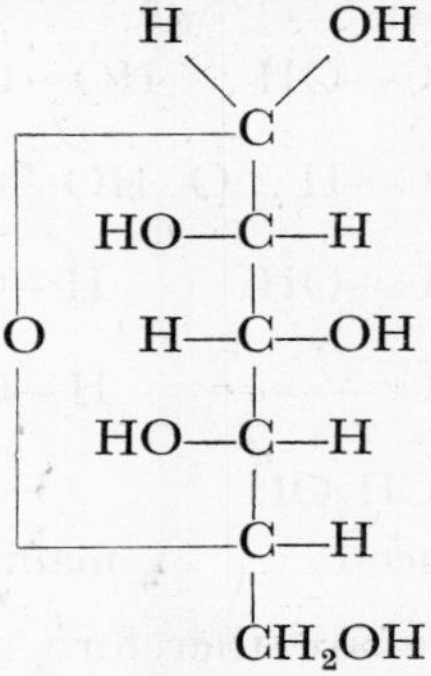

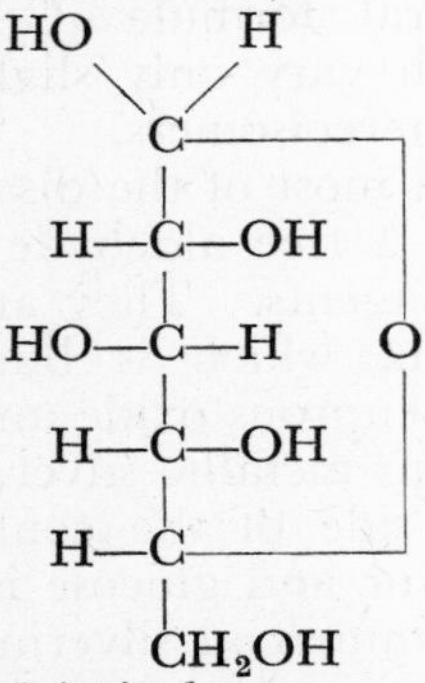

$\beta\ (+)$ glucose $\beta\ (-)$ glucose

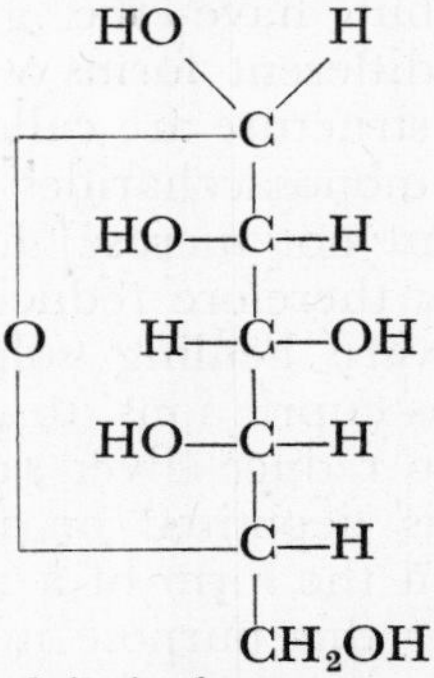

If H and OH are interchanged on carbon atom 2 of glucose without altering any other part of the molecule, the resulting compound has now completely different properties and is, in fact, the sugar mannose. Similar changes on other carbon atoms of the molecule give rise to other sugars, among them galactose.

$$
\begin{array}{ccc}
\text{H}\quad\text{OH} & \text{H}\quad\text{OH} & \text{H}\quad\text{OH} \\
\text{C} & \text{C} & \text{C} \\
\text{H--C--OH} & \text{HO--C--H} & \text{H--C--OH} \\
\text{HO--C--H}\quad\text{O} & \text{HO--C--H}\quad\text{O} & \text{HO--C--H}\quad\text{O} \\
\text{H--C--OH} & \text{H--C--OH} & \text{HO--C--H} \\
\text{H--C} & \text{H--C} & \text{H--C} \\
\text{CH}_2\text{OH} & \text{CH}_2\text{OH} & \text{CH}_2\text{OH} \\
\text{glucose} & \text{mannose} & \text{galactose}
\end{array}
$$

There are therefore a large number of hexoses which differ only slightly in structure from each other but have the general formula $C_6H_{12}O_6$. These different forms which vary only slightly in spatial structure are called stereoisomers.

The monosaccharides and most of the disaccharides (but not sucrose) have a free aldehyde group and are therefore reducing agents. They are able to convert Fehling solution, which is blue and contains cupric ions, to red cuprous oxide and they can also reduce silver salts to metallic silver. The metal is deposited on the side of the containing vessel in the form of a mirror and glucose is often used for this purpose in commercial silvering processes.

Glucose gives rise to gluconic acid by mild oxidation but, under more violent conditions, saccharic acid is formed. Another oxidized form of glucose, glucuronic acid, is used by the body for detoxication purposes. (See Chapter III).

```
      COOH              COOH              CHO
       |                 |                 |
   H—C—OH            H—C—OH            H—C—OH
       |                 |                 |
  HO—C—H            HO—C—H            HO—C—H
       |                 |                 |
   H—C—OH            H—C—OH            H—C—OH
       |                 |                 |
   H—C—OH            H—C—OH            H—C—OH
       |                 |                 |
    CH₂OH             COOH              COOH
 gluconic acid    saccharic acid    glucuronic acid
```

An amino derivative of glucose—glucosamine, is an important constituent of chitin, which forms the structural material of the shell of insects and crustaceans.

```
          CHO
           |
      H—C—NH₂
           |
     HO—C—H
           |
      H—C—OH        glucosamine
           |
      H—C—OH
           |
        CH₂OH
```

Many compounds, particularly in the plant kingdom are found combined with glucose or other sugars. They are known as glucosides if their sugar component is glucose but collectively they are termed glycosides and they may be joined by α- or β- linkages.

α-glucosides are hydrolysed by the enzyme maltase, an α-glucosidase of the intestinal juice, while the enzyme emulsin present in bitter almonds catalyzes the hydrolysis of β-glucosides.

Fructose.

This sugar also called laevulose because of its laevorotatory property is present in sweet fruits, honey and combined with glucose in the disaccharide —sucrose. It is also found in foetal* mammalian blood, and in seminal fluid where it helps to nourish the spermatozoa.

Fructose is a ketone alcohol (ketose) as opposed to glucose which is an aldehyde alcohol (aldose).

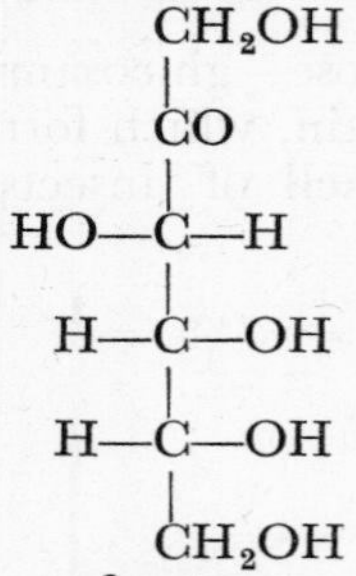

$$
\begin{array}{cc}
CH_2OH & CH_2OH \\
| & | \\
CO & HO—C———\\
| & | \\
HO—C—H & HO—C—H \\
| & | \\
H—C—OH & H—C—OH \quad O \\
| & | \\
H—C—OH & H—C—OH \\
| & | \\
CH_2OH & CH_2— \\
\text{fructose} & \text{fructose} \\
\text{(open chain form} & \text{(ring form)}
\end{array}
$$

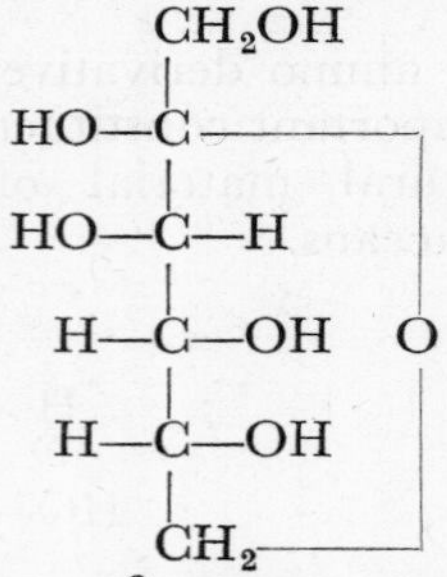

Galactose.

Yet another monosaccharide, galactose, occurs in the body only in combined form as a constituent of lactose (milk sugar) and as galactosides in nervous tissue.

* A foetus is the unborn young of an animal.

Pentoses.

So far only sugars with 6 carbon atoms (hexoses) have been considered but there are several bio-chemically important sugars, the pentoses, which contain 5 carbon atoms.

Examples are ribose, arabinose and xylose and most of them do not occur free in nature but are liberated on hydrolysis from various vegetable gums.

Ribose, it will be remembered, is present in **NAD** and **NADP**, and the nucleic acids also contain this sugar as well as its close relative, deoxyribose.

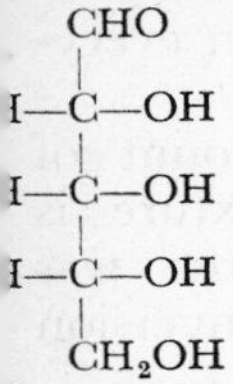

ribose
(open chain form)   ribose
(ring form)   deoxyribose
(ring form)

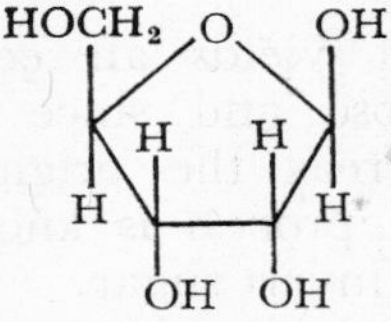

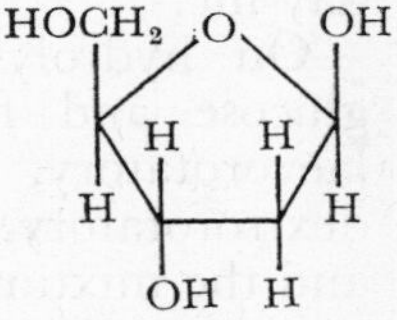

Pentoses may appear in the urine after the in-gestion of large amounts of certain fruits such as cherries or plums (alimentary pentosuria) but this condition may also result from an " inborn error of metabolism ".   In this inherited type of pentosuria, pentose sugars are excreted independently of the nature of the diet.

Pentoses are generally found in a five-membered (furanose) ring form, as shown above, when com-bined with other substances.

The disaccharides.

These compounds as the name implies are made up of two monosaccharide units and in fact may be considered as sugar glycosides. Their general formula, $C_{12}H_{22}O_{11}$, is twice that of a monosaccharide minus a molecule of water.

$$2 \; (C_6H_{12}O_6) - H_2O = C_{12}H_{22}O_{11}$$

From the biochemical viewpoint the three most important disaccharides are sucrose, maltose and lactose.

Sucrose.

Often called cane sugar, sucrose is found in large amounts in sugar cane and beet as well as in many other plants. It is a white crystalline solid with a sweet taste and is, in fact, the sugar used in everyday life.

On hydrolysis it yields an equal amount of glucose and fructose and since this mixture is laevorotatory, whereas the original sucrose was dextrorotatory, the process is known as inversion and the mixture as invert sugar.

Sucrose is non-reducing because it has no free aldehyde groups (see structure below) and it should also be noted that its fructose component which exists as a six-membered (pyranose) ring in the free state is present in its five-membered (furanose) ring form.

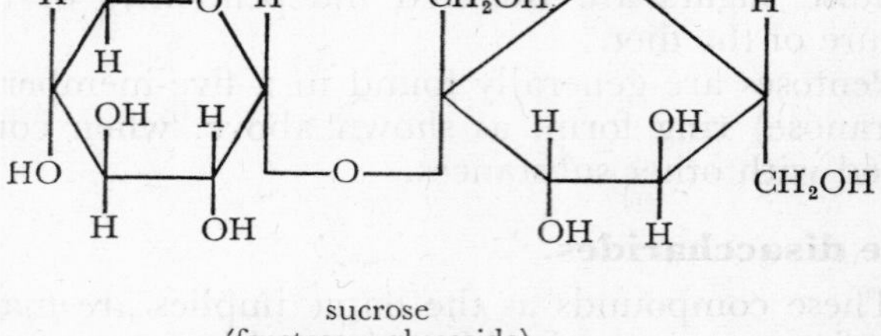

sucrose
(fructose-α-glucoside)

The enzyme which catalyzes this hydrolysis, sucrase

or invertase, is found in yeast, higher plants and in the intestinal juice of mammals.

Barley sugar is sucrose heated to about 150°C and at 200°C it forms caramel.

Although sucrose is a relatively simple molecule, it took many years to achieve its total synthesis in the laboratory.

Maltose.

This disaccharide does not usually occur free and is produced from starch or glycogen by the enzyme amylase. It is a reducing sugar made up of two molecules of glucose which it yields on hydrolysis with acid or the enzyme maltase.

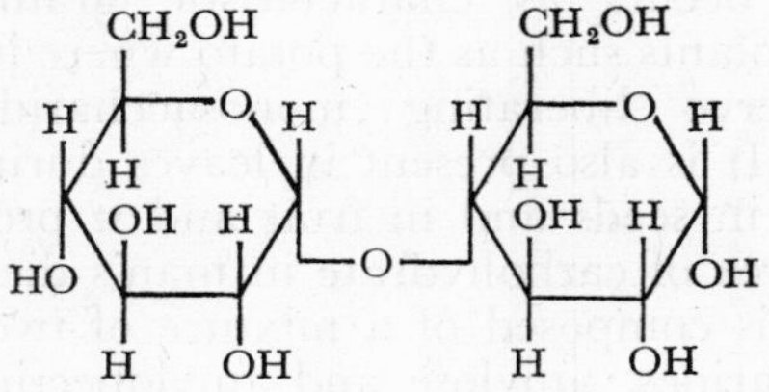

maltose
(glucose-α-glucoside)

Lactose.

Often called milk sugar, this disaccharide occurs only in milk and is produced commercially as a by-product in the manufacture of cheese. It is a reducing sugar which on hydrolysis yields glucose and galactose.

The degree of sweetness of the various mono- and disaccharides in decreasing order is as follows:

1) fructose   4) maltose
2) sucrose   5) galactose
3) glucose   6) lactose

The polysaccharides.

The polysaccharides are large complex molecules made up of many monosaccharide units and they differ considerably in properties from the simple sugars. Thus, they tend to form particulate (colloidal) rather than true solutions and do not possess reducing properties or a sweet taste. Many types of polysaccharides are known and those of biochemical importance include starch, glycogen and cellulose, all three of which are composed entirely of glucose units.

Starch.

Starch occurs as characteristic grains in the tubers of plants such as the potato where it acts as a food reserve liberating monosaccharides when needed. It is also present in leaves during photosynthesis, in seeds and in fruit and it provides the main source of carbohydrate in man's diet.

Starch is composed of a mixture of two types of polysaccharides, amylose and amylopectin, both of which yield glucose on complete hydrolysis.

These two polysaccharides differ from each other only in the way their monosaccharide constituents are linked together.

Amylose is a straight chain compound made up of about 200–300 α linked glucose molecules whereas amylopectin is a highly branched substance with chains of 20–24 glucose units.

The characteristic blue colour that starch gives with iodine is due to its amylose component, the very much longer amylopectin molecule giving a reddish brown colour with this reagent.

Two types of enzymes, the α- and β-amylases, produced by animals and germinating seeds respectively, catalyze the hydrolysis of starch (latin—amylum). The α-variety, also called dextrinogenic amylase, helps to split amylose and amylopectin randomly forming small starch-like molecules called

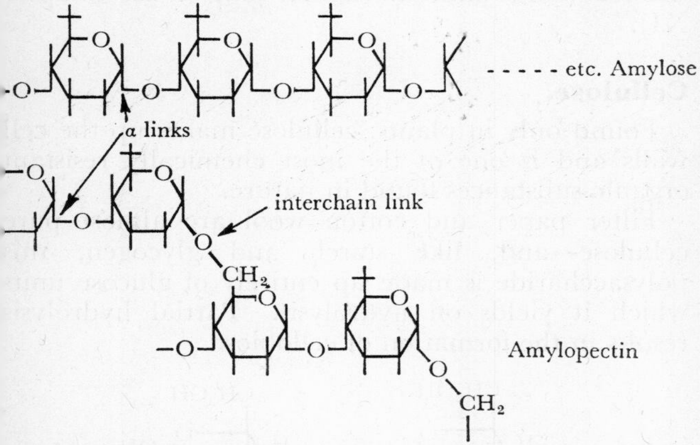

- - - - - etc. Amylose

α links

interchain link

Amylopectin

dextrins, whereas β-amylase, also known as maltogenic amylase, is responsible for splitting off maltose molecules one at a time.

The enzyme maltase completes this hydrolysis by converting maltose to glucose.

α-amylase is present in saliva and in pancreatic juice.

Glycogen.

Often called animal starch, glycogen is the main form in which glucose is stored in the body where it occurs chiefly in the liver and muscles. It is very much like the amylopectin of starch in structure though even more highly branched and like amylopectin it gives a deep red brown colour with iodine solution. It is attacked by the same digestive enzymes that will attack starch and it is eventually broken down to maltose by them.

Another enzyme, phosphorylase, breaks down glycogen to glucose phosphate inside the cells and this reaction is under hormonal control (see Chapter XI).

Cellulose.

Found only in plants, cellulose makes up the cell walls and is one of the most chemically resistant organic substances found in nature.

Filter paper and cotton wool are almost pure cellulose—and, like starch and glycogen, this polysaccharide is made up entirely of glucose units which it yields on hydrolysis. Partial hydrolysis results in the formation of cellobiose.

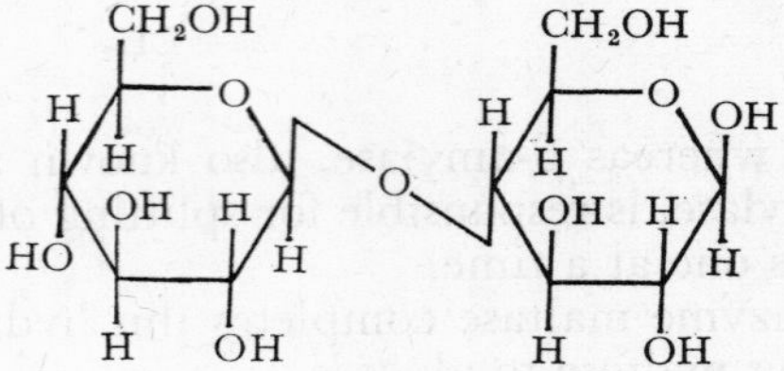

cellobiose
(glucose-β-glucoside)

Cellulose is unbranched and consists of long parallel chains of β-linked glucose units held together in bundles by special bonds (hydrogen bonds) which give the compound its remarkable tensile strength.

Enzymes capable of hydrolysing cellulose, the cellulases, are present only in microorganisms, large numbers of which inhabit the alimentary tract of herbivores such as the cow and make up what is known as their intestinal flora.

In the gut, they digest the cellulose of grass and pass on many of the breakdown products to the host in return for shelter and a certain amount of food. Such an association which is beneficial to both the herbivore and the inhabiting micro-organism is called symbiosis.

Enzymes capable of breaking down cellulose are also present in some snails.

Other polysaccharides include inulin which is composed entirely of fructose units and is found in dahlias, dandelions and Jerusalem artichokes; chitin which makes up the outerskeleton of insects, lobsters, crabs, etc., and various gums such as gum arabic which is made up mainly of pentoses. The pectins present in fruits are also polysaccharides and are used for making jam since they readily form gels when mixed with sugar.

CHAPTER VII

CARBOHYDRATE METABOLISM

Digestion and absorption.

THE carbohydrates present in a mixed diet consist mainly of starch together with glucose and fructose from fruits and honey, lactose from milk, and cellulose and sucrose.

In man and herbivores, starch is partly digested by a salivary amylase, ptyalin, which is absent from many carnivores including the dog.

If starch is kept in the mouth for a minute or two and then expelled, it will be found to have entirely disappeared and its place taken by reducing sugars consisting mainly of maltose. Although ptyalin is rapidly destroyed by the hydrochloric acid of the stomach, its digestive action nevertheless continues there because the swallowed food mass is only penetrated slowly by the gastric juices.

There are no carbohydrate-digesting enzymes in the stomach and any hydrolysis catalyzed by hydrochloric acid is so slow at body temperature that it can virtually be ignored.

The final and most important site of carbohydrate digestion is the small intestine where in the presence of the very active α-amylase of pancreatic juice together with the maltase, sucrase (invertase) and lactase of intestinal juice (succus entericus), the process of hydrolysis to monosaccharides is completed.

Absorption also takes place in the small intestine and it is remarkable that only monosaccharides—not even disaccharides—will pass through the intestinal wall into the blood. Certain sugars are absorbed more rapidly than others and the order in decreasing rates of absorption is: (1) galactose, (2) glucose, (3) fructose, (4) pentoses. It is thought that a process of phosphorylation, i.e. the addition of phosphoric acid on to the sugar molecule is involved in active absorption.

However, since starch forms the bulk of our dietary carbohydrate, most of the absorbed monosaccharide consists of glucose.

Storage as glycogen.

The glucose that has been absorbed from the intestine is carried by the blood to the liver where some is converted to glycogen and stored until needed by the body. The remainder passes into the general circulation and is either oxidized by the tissues to carbon dioxide and water or else converted to fat.

Glycogen formed from glucose in blood is also present in muscle but unlike liver glycogen it is not reconverted to sugar but is broken down to lactic acid during violent muscular activity. Lactic acid, however, can be converted to glycogen in the liver so that muscle glycogen gives rise to glucose only indirectly.

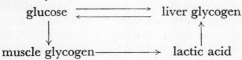

Blood glucose.

The sugar in blood is virtually all glucose and its level is remarkably constant under normal conditions rarely rising above or falling much below 100 milligrams per 100 millilitres of blood. It is present in both the red cells and the plasma.

After a heavy meal, however, the blood sugar level rises considerably and then falls back to normal within about two hours.

Normally, equilibrium is maintained between the factors that tend to elevate the concentration of glucose in blood (hyperglycaemia) such as absorption from the intestine or its formation from liver glycogen and other sources, and those tending to lower the blood sugar level (i.e., to cause hypoglycaemia) such as storage in liver and muscle, oxidation by tissues and conversion into fat. Many of these factors are under the control of hormones, substances produced by the endocrine glands (see Chapter XI) that circulate in the blood acting as chemical regulators. Hormones which influence carbohydrate metabolism include insulin, adrenaline, glucagon, growth hormone and certain steroids (see Chapter VIII) produced by the outer layer (cortex) of the adrenal glands.

At and below the normal concentration of glucose, the kidneys, which act as a filter, prevent any glucose from passing into the urine by reabsorbing it, but in hyperglycaemia excess sugar spills over, resulting in glycosuria, i.e. sugar in the urine. The concentration at which blood glucose is no longer retained by the kidneys is known as its renal threshold.

In a harmless hereditary condition known as renal glycosuria and after the administration of certain drugs such as phlorizin, the kidney threshold for glucose is lowered and sugar appears in the urine even though the blood glucose concentration is normal. This threshold may also be lowered in pregnancy and in certain diseases.

Glycosuria from these causes must not be confused with the glycosuria of sugar diabetes due to a disturbance in carbohydrate metabolism. In this disease there is a deficiency of the hormone insulin which normally controls the breakdown of glucose and the amount that is deposited as glycogen in liver and muscles. Insulin is produced by certain cells of the pancreas and injection of this hormone immediately causes a decrease in the high blood glucose concentration characteristic of diabetes.

Too much of the hormone, however, produces hypoglycaemia, so that diabetics always carry glucose with them to counter any such effect.

Severe hypoglycaemia is accompanied by shock and insulin has been used in attempts to cure certain types of mental disorder

The breakdown of glucose.

Although the total oxidation of glucose in the living organism may be represented by the equation:

$$C_6H_{12}O_6 + 6O_2 \longrightarrow 6CO_2 + 6H_2O$$

the actual process takes place in a large number of separate steps and may be divided into:

a) anaerobic reactions i.e. the breakdown of glucose without the participation of oxygen;

b) aerobic reactions i.e. the oxidation of the products formed during anaerobic breakdown.

In the absence of oxygen, glucose is converted to ethyl alcohol and carbon dioxide by the enzymes of yeast while, under similar conditions, muscle and other animal tissues convert glucose to lactic acid. The former process is known as fermentation and the latter as glycolysis, but they are very similar and proceed as far as pyruvic acid by a common pathway.

G

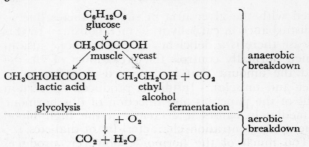

The anaerobic breakdown of glucose.
Alcoholic fermentation.

Most of the early work on the reactions involved in the breakdown of glucose was carried out with cell-free yeast juice which converts this sugar to ethyl alcohol and carbon dioxide. This process is called alcoholic fermentation.

$$C_6H_{12}O_6 \longrightarrow 2CH_3CH_2OH + 2CO_2$$
$$\text{glucose} \qquad\qquad \text{ethyl alcohol}$$

It was noticed during these experiments that, after a time, the rate of carbon dioxide production, which can easily be followed by the effervescence of the glucose solution, decreased and the reaction stopped unless soluble inorganic phosphate was added. The recovery was only temporary, however, and since the added phosphate soon disappeared it was inferred that sugar phosphates might be formed as intermediate breakdown products. Several such compounds were eventually isolated and the sequence in which they were formed during the breakdown of glucose worked out (see below) and shown to be catalyzed by enzymes occurring in yeast juice.

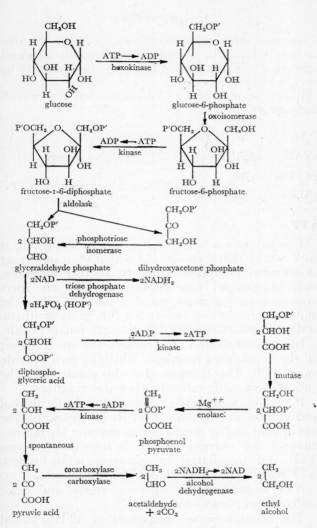

The breakdown of glucose by fermentation

Various other substances such as NAD, cocarboxylase (vitamin B_1 phosphate) magnesium ions and adenosine triphosphate (ATP) were also found to be essential in fermentation.

It can be seen from the diagram that the overall reaction is:

$$C_6H_{12}O_6 \rightarrow 2C_2H_5OH + 2CO_2$$

$$2NAD \rightarrow 2NADH_2 \rightarrow 2NAD \qquad \therefore \text{ No change}$$

$$\left. \begin{array}{l} 2ATP \rightarrow 2ADP \\ 4ADP \rightarrow 4ATP \end{array} \right\} \quad \therefore \text{ A gain of 2 molecules of ATP.}$$

ATP.

This substance, found universally in living cells is an " energy rich " compound which by transferring its terminal phosphate group to another molecule, such as glucose, can convert a relatively inert substance into a more reactive one. ATP is the immediate source of energy for the many synthetic and other reactions needed for the maintenance of life.

In fermentation ATP provides the spark to set off the breakdown reactions, which in turn provide more ATP. This compound is also essential for the initiation of many other biochemical reactions.

If glucose were broken down directly to alcohol and carbon dioxide, much of its energy would be lost as heat but by means of this stepwise breakdown most of the energy released is incorporated into ATP and transferred to wherever it is needed. ATP itself is converted to ADP in this process.

ATP is made up of adenine, ribose and three molecules of phosphoric acid:

The adenine-ribose component of ATP is called adenosine.

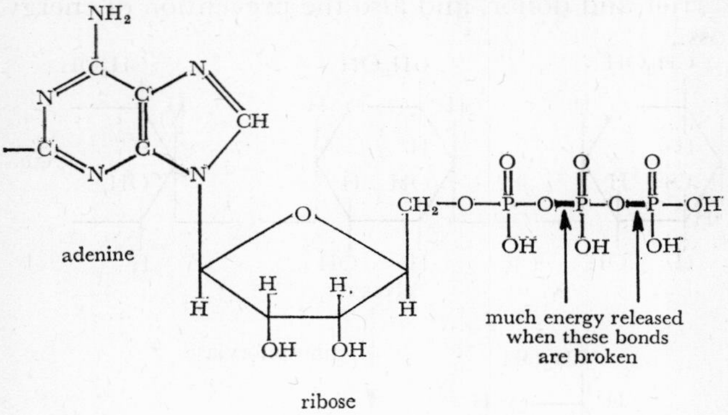

adenine

ribose

much energy released
when these bonds
are broken

Glycolysis.

In animals and man, the glycogen of liver and muscle is broken down anaerobically to lactic acid by a process very similar to fermentation, which differs only initially and after the pyruvic acid stage. It is known as glycolysis. Glycogen is first broken down to glucose–1–phosphate which is then converted to glucose–6–phosphate, both reactions being enzyme catalyzed. The latter compound is then converted to pyruvic acid by exactly the same steps as in fermentation but is then reduced to lactic acid instead of being decarboxylated to acetaldehyde (see fermentation) and reduced to alcohol.

Glucose too is broken down in this way since the enzyme hexokinase which converts glucose to glucose–6–phosphate is present in animals as in yeast and it is remarkable that carbohydrates should be degraded by us in a way very similar to the one used by lowly organisms such as yeast.

In both instances however the ultimate aim is the production of ATP, i.e. the formation of an energy carrier and donor, and also the prevention of energy loss.

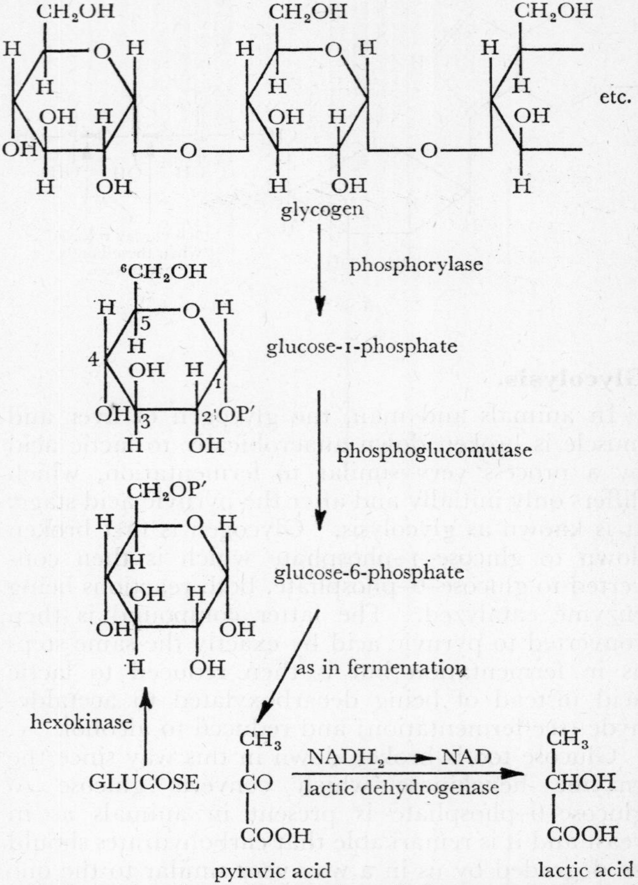

glycogen

phosphorylase

glucose-1-phosphate

phosphoglucomutase

glucose-6-phosphate

as in fermentation

hexokinase

GLUCOSE

$NADH_2 \longrightarrow NAD$

lactic dehydrogenase

pyruvic acid

lactic acid

Before leaving the topic of fermentation and glycolysis it must be pointed out that most of the reactions described so far are reversible and that any of the compounds in this metabolic pathway as well as many others can give rise to glycogen in the liver. However, the synthesis of glycogen from glucose–1–phosphate is not the reverse of the phosphorylase reaction but a complex process involving uridine triphosphate (UTP) and the formation of uridine diphosphate glucose as intermediate. It is a general biochemical principle that synthetic pathways differ at some point from the reverse of the degradative pathways. This is also illustrated by the findings that pyruvate must first be converted to oxaloacetate (see below) before it can form phosphoenol pyruvate and be resynthesized to glycogen.

Sucrose, maltose, lactose, fructose and galactose also enter the general glycolytic chain and whether glucose and these compounds are broken down further or converted to glycogen will depend on the nutritional state of the animal, i.e. whether it is building up carbohydrate reserves or is breaking them down to provide energy.

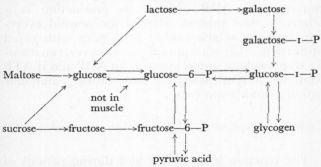

As already mentioned, the reaction glucose⟶ glycogen is irreversible in muscle but in the liver glycogen is easily reconverted to glucose.

Muscular activity.

Muscle may be considered as a highly specialized machine constructed from organic materials which utilizes chemical energy to perform mechanical work. Since muscular activity requires the expenditure of energy it might be assumed that ATP plays an important role, which indeed it does.

Muscle is largely made up of the elastic protein actomyosin and it has been shown that isolated fibrils of this compound will contract when placed in a solution containing ATP. In fact, since the myosin component of actomyosin exhibits ATPase activity, it has been suggested that muscular activity can be represented as changes in the physical properties of this protein resulting from its enzymic action on ATP.

However, besides ATP, the muscle of vertebrates contain another very important energy-rich compound, creatine phosphate, which acts as an energy reserve. During severe muscular exertion, the small amount of ATP present in muscle is soon converted to ADP because its production is a relatively slow process adapted for normal everyday activities which cannot keep pace with rapid utilization. Creatine phosphate, however, can transfer its phosphate group instantly to ADP and if ATP were not resynthesized in this manner, muscular activity would soon cease.

$$\text{Creatine phosphate} + \text{ADP} \underset{\longleftarrow}{\overset{\longrightarrow}{\text{enzyme}}} \text{creatine} + \text{ATP}$$

The reaction is reversible and during periods of rest enough ATP is formed to convert creatine back to creatine phosphate.

In invertebrates, arginine phosphate replaces

creatine phosphate but acts in exactly the same way and these two compounds are also known as phosphagens.

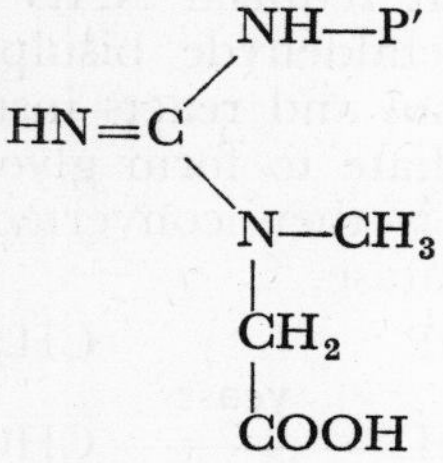

$$HN=C \begin{array}{c} NH-P' \\ | \\ N-CH_3 \\ | \\ CH_2 \\ | \\ COOH \end{array} \qquad HN=C \begin{array}{c} NH-P' \\ | \\ NH \\ | \\ (CH_2)_3 \\ | \\ CHNH_2 \\ | \\ COOH \end{array}$$

creatine phosphate 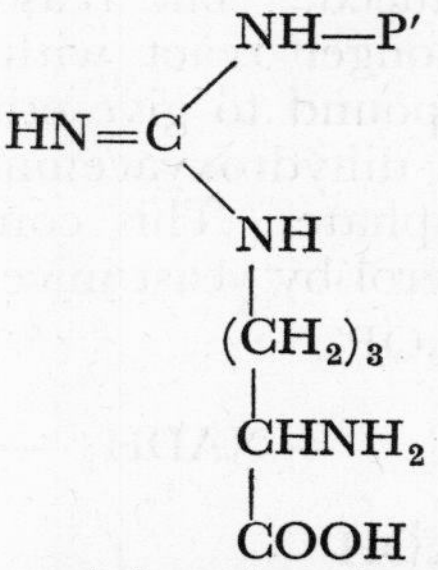   arginine phosphate

The greatest amount of phosphagen is present in those muscles which are the most powerful and it is also present in the electric organs of certain fishes and in spermatozoa which need much energy for their locomotion.

Finally it might be mentioned that during severe exercise more lactic acid is produced than can be oxidized or used up in synthetic reactions with the result that it accumulates and is partly responsible for the feeling of fatigue.

The formation of glycerol from glucose.

It will be remembered that at one stage of the fermentative breakdown of glucose by yeast juice enzymes, dihydroxyacetone phosphate is formed (see diagram on fermentation) which is then rapidly converted to glyceraldehyde phosphate. At a little later stage NAD is reduced but is then re-oxidized when acetaldehyde is converted to ethyl alcohol.

If sodium bisulphite ($NaHSO_3$) which combines with acetaldehyde is added to the reaction mixture, a large amount of glycerol and no ethyl alcohol is produced. The reason is that reduced NAD can no longer react with the acetaldehyde bisulphite compound to give ethyl alcohol and reacts instead with dihydroxyacetone phosphate to form glycerol phosphate. This compound is then converted to glycerol by yeast juice phosphatase.

$$
\begin{array}{ccccc}
\text{CH}_2\text{OP}' & & \text{CH}_2\text{OP}' & & \text{CH}_2\text{OH} \\
| & & | & \text{yeast} & | \\
\text{CO} & + \text{NADH}_2 \longrightarrow & \text{CHOH} & \xrightarrow{\hspace{1cm}} & \text{CHOH} \\
| & & | & \text{phosphatase} & | \\
\text{CH}_2\text{OH} & & \text{CH}_2\text{OH} & & \text{CH}_2\text{OH} \\
\text{dihydroxyacetone} & & \text{glycerol} & & \text{glycerol} \\
\text{phosphate} & & \text{phosphate} & &
\end{array}
$$

The explosive, nitroglycerine, is made from glycerol normally obtained from fats, but when Germany in the 1914–18 war was blockaded and this source of glycerol was in great shortage, it was produced from carbohydrate by the method just described.

This provides a good example of how research findings which at first appear to be of purely academic interest can turn out to be very important indeed.

The aerobic breakdown of glucose.

So far only that part of the metabolism of glucose has been described which does not require oxygen but under normal conditions this sugar is completely broken down oxidatively to carbon dioxide and water.

In muscle no lactic acid is formed when there is an ample supply of oxygen and pyruvic acid is the product which is further degraded (see below).

Overall pyruvic acid is oxidized to carbon

dioxide and water and this reaction was found to be catalyzed by small amounts of oxaloacetate.

$$2CH_3COCOOH + 5O_2 \longrightarrow 6CO_2 + 4H_2O$$

Active acetate, derived from pyruvate by a complex reaction involving coenzyme A and several other coenzymes, first combines with oxaloacetate to form citrate. Pyruvate also gives rise to oxaloacetate by a reaction involving CO_2 and the enzyme oxaloacetic decarboxylase.

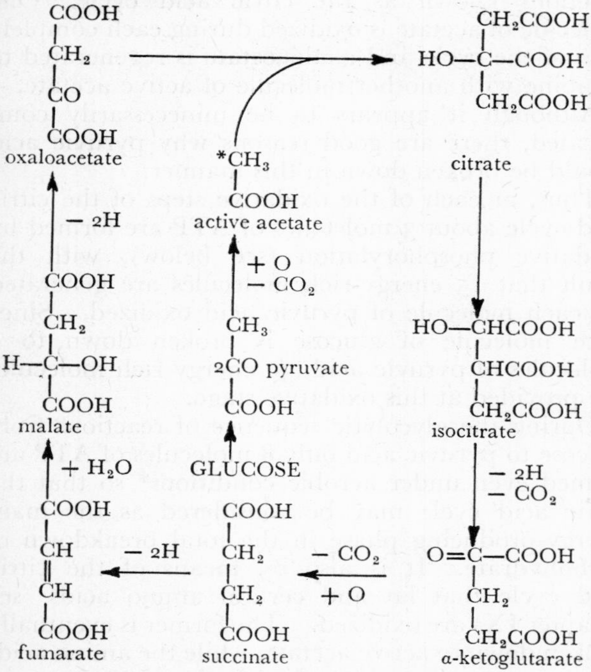

The citric acid cycle

* This compound is really acetyl coenzyme A but it acts as if it were simply highly reactive acetic acid.

$$
\begin{array}{ccc}
\text{CH}_3 & & \text{COOH} \\
| & \text{oxaloacetic} & | \\
\text{CO} \quad + \text{CO}_2 \rightleftharpoons & & \text{CH}_2 \\
| & \text{decarboxylase} & | \\
\text{COOH} & & \text{CO} \\
& & | \\
& & \text{COOH}
\end{array}
$$

pyruvic acid   oxaloacetic acid

Citrate is then further degraded by a sequence of reactions known as the citric acid cycle. One molecule of acetate is oxidized during each complete turn of the cycle and oxaloacetate is regenerated to combine with another molecule of active acetate.

Although it appears to be unnecessarily complicated, there are good reasons why pyruvic acid should be broken down in this manner.

Thus, at each of the oxidative steps of the citric acid cycle about 3 molecules of ATP are formed by oxidative phosphorylation (see below), with the result that 15 energy-rich molecules are generated for each molecule of pyruvic acid oxidized. Since each molecule of glucose is broken down to 2 molecules of pyruvic acid, 30 energy rich molecules are provided at this oxidative stage.

During the glycolytic sequence of reactions from glucose to pyruvic acid only 8 molecules of ATP are formed even under aerobic conditions* so that the citric acid cycle may be considered as the main energy-producing phase in the total breakdown of carbohydrate. It is also by means of the citric acid cycle that fat and certain amino acids (see Chapter IX) are oxidized. The former is eventually broken down to active acetate, while the amino acids alanine, aspartic acid and glutamic acid are con-

* Under anaerobic conditions only 2 molecules of ATP are formed.

verted by oxidative deamination (i.e. removal of the
—NH_2 group followed by oxidation) or by transamination (see Chapter IX) to pyruvic, oxaloacetic
and α-ketoglutaric acids respectively. These products which are components of the citric acid cycle
are then oxidized to CO_2 and water, or converted to
glycogen in the manner already described.

$$\underset{\text{alanine}}{\begin{array}{c} CH_3 \\ | \\ CHNH_2 \\ | \\ COOH \end{array}} + \tfrac{1}{2} O_2 \xrightarrow[\text{enzyme}]{} \underset{\text{pyruvic acid}}{\begin{array}{c} CH_3 \\ | \\ CO \\ | \\ COOH \end{array}} + NH_3$$

$$\underset{\text{aspartic acid}}{\begin{array}{c} COOH \\ | \\ CH_2 \\ | \\ CHNH_2 \\ | \\ COOH \end{array}} + \tfrac{1}{2} O_2 \xrightarrow[\text{enzyme}]{} \underset{\text{oxaloacetic acid}}{\begin{array}{c} COOH \\ | \\ CH_2 \\ | \\ CO \\ | \\ COOH \end{array}} + NH_3$$

$$\underset{\text{glutamic acid}}{\begin{array}{c} COOH \\ | \\ CH_2 \\ | \\ CH_2 \\ | \\ CHNH_2 \\ | \\ COOH \end{array}} + \tfrac{1}{2} O_2 \xrightarrow[\text{enzyme}]{} \underset{\alpha\text{-ketoglutaric acid}}{\begin{array}{c} COOH \\ | \\ CH_2 \\ | \\ CH_2 \\ | \\ CO \\ | \\ COOH \end{array}} + NH_3$$

Two names stand out in connection with the citric
acid cycle—those of Krebs and Szent Gyorgyi, both
Nobel prize winners.

Oxidative phosphorylation.

The enzymes which catalyze the citric acid cycle reactions as well as many oxidizing enzymes are localized within the mitochondria and it is in these subcellular particles, which act as the " powerhouse " of the cell, that most of the ATP is generated.

When a substance is oxidized its hydrogen atoms or electrons are transferred to oxygen along an organized system of enzymes known as the respiratory chain. It is during this process that ATP is produced by oxidative phosphorylation. The exact manner in which this occurs is still a matter of speculation but 3 molecules of ATP are formed for every 2 atoms of hydrogen oxidized by the full respiratory chain which includes $NADH_2$ dehydrogenase, flavoprotein and cytochrome oxidase (see Chapter V).

A number of compounds such as dinitrophenol and the hormone, thyroxine, are able to " uncouple " oxidation from phosphorylation and, under these circumstances, the energy of the respiratory process is not trapped in ATP but is wasted as heat.

CHAPTER VIII

THE LIPIDS

THE lipids include not only the true fats but also compounds which are either chemically related or else found in association with them on account of similar solubilities. They may be divided into 3 groups:

1) Simple lipids: *a*) Fats,
   b) Waxes.
2) Compound lipids: *a*) Phospholipids,
   b) Glycolipids.
3) Steroids.

The Fats.

The fats (or vegetable and animal oils if liquid) are glyceryl esters which on hydrolysis yield glycerol and fatty acids. This can be accomplished by using acid, alkali (saponification), superheated steam or the appropriate enzyme—the lipase of the pancreas.

$$\begin{matrix} CH_2OOCR \\ | \\ CHOOCR \\ | \\ CH_2OOCR \\ \text{fat} \end{matrix} + 3H_2O \longrightarrow \begin{matrix} CH_2OH \\ | \\ CHOH \\ | \\ CH_2OH \\ \text{glycerol} \end{matrix} + \begin{matrix} 3RCOOH \\ \text{fatty acid} \end{matrix}$$

In the animal kingdom they form the fatty tissues of the body and in plants occur chiefly in spores, seeds, e.g. cotton, sunflower, linseed, and coats of fruit, e.g. palm and olive. They form some of the food reserves for the plant embryo during germination and early growth.

The most important and widely distributed fatty acids in fat are palmitic, stearic and oleic acids though a large number of other similar compounds exist in nature.

$$C_{15}H_{31}COOH \qquad C_{17}H_{35}COOH \qquad C_{17}H_{33}COOH$$
Palmitic   Stearic   Oleic
acid   acid   acid

It is important to note that each of these acids contains an even number of carbon atoms and that fats from acids containing an odd number of carbon atoms are virtually unknown in nature. This fact, as it will be seen later, throws some light on fat synthesis by living organisms.

Palmitic acid which is the major constituent of the fatty acids of palm olive has been reported as a component of almost all fats whereas stearic acid is more abundant in the fats of animals. Oleic acid, however, is the most widely distributed and since it has two hydrogen atoms less than stearic acid, it contains a double bond and therefore belongs to the unsaturated fatty acid series.

$$CH_3(CH_2)_7CH=CH(CH_2)_7COOH \text{ oleic acid}$$

The hardness and melting point of a particular fat depends on the relative proportions of these fatty acids. Thus beef fat which contains more oleic acid than mutton fat has a lower melting point than the latter while olive oil which is an oil at room temperature, contains practically only oleic acid. In general, the greater the degree of unsaturation, the lower the melting point.

Hydrogen gas under pressure in the presence of finely divided nickel as catalyst converts unsaturated fatty acids to the saturated compounds and it is by this hydrogenation process that lard and butter substitutes, e.g. margarine, are produced commercially from unsaturated vegetable oils.

So far only the simple straight chain fatty acids have been mentioned but there are several which are either branched, cyclic or highly unsaturated.

Tuberculostearic and phthioic acids which have been isolated from the tubercle bacillus are examples of branched fatty acids and these compounds on injection into animals can bring about some of the typical leasons of tuberculosis.

Chaulmoogric acid present in chaulmoogra oil (from the seeds of certain trees in Burma) is a cyclic acid which has been widely used in the treatment of leprosy while some of the highly unsaturated acids are " essential fatty acids " because the body needs them but is unable to synthesize them.

$$
\begin{array}{l}
CH{=}{=}{=}CH \\
\mid \qquad\quad\; \mid \qquad\quad CH(CH_2)_{12}COOH \quad\text{Chaulmoogric} \\
\qquad\qquad\qquad\qquad\qquad\qquad\qquad\qquad\quad\text{acid} \\
CH_2{-}{-}CH_2
\end{array}
$$

It has also been shown that unsaturated fatty acids in the diet can prevent the onset of arteriosclerosis, i.e. hardening of the arteries with deposition of cholesterol (see later).

Another fatty acid, ricinoleic acid, is responsible for the purgative action of castor oil.

The Waxes.

The waxes are fatty esters of long-chain alcohols other than glycerol. Examples include wool wax obtained from wool grease (lanolin), beeswax, and spermaceti which is a mixture of waxes found inside the skull of the sperm whale.

The waxes have higher melting points than the fats and are resistant to lipases (fat-digesting enzymes).

The Phospholipids.

The phospholipids, which may be subdivided into the lecithins and cephalins, are made up of glycerol, phosphoric acid, fatty acids, and either choline (lecithins), or some compound other than choline such as the amino acid serine (cephalins).

$$
\begin{array}{l}
\mathrm{CH_2OOCR} \\
\mathrm{RCOOCH} \qquad \mathrm{O} \qquad\qquad\qquad \mathrm{CH_3} \\
\qquad\quad \underset{\parallel}{} \qquad\qquad \overset{+}{} \\
\mathrm{CH_2O{-}P{-}OCH_2CH_2N{-}CH_3} \\
\qquad\quad\;\; \mathrm{OH} \qquad\qquad\qquad \mathrm{CH_3} \\
\qquad\qquad\quad \text{lecithin}
\end{array}
$$

The acetyl derivative of choline—acetylcholine, is the substance which is released at most nerve endings when nerves are stimulated.

Lecithin is a common cell constituent but is especially abundant in brain tissue, egg yolk and the seeds of plants. It is also an important constituent of the cell membrane.

Lecithinase, an enzyme present in the venom of cobra and rattlesnake, liberates one molecule of fatty acid from lecithin and thus changes it to lysolecithin which is a strong detergent and potent haemolytic agent (i.e. disrupts red blood corpuscles).

The glycolipids.

Substances of this class present mainly in brain and nervous tissue are composed of fatty acids, the sugar galactose (sometimes glucose) and a complex basic compound—sphingosine.

Examples are phrenosin and kerasin but virtually nothing is known about their biochemical role.

The Steroids.

The steroids which include the sterols, the bile acids, the sex and adrenocortical hormones, the cardiac glycosides and vitamin D, are complex organic compounds which all possess structures related to cholesterol.

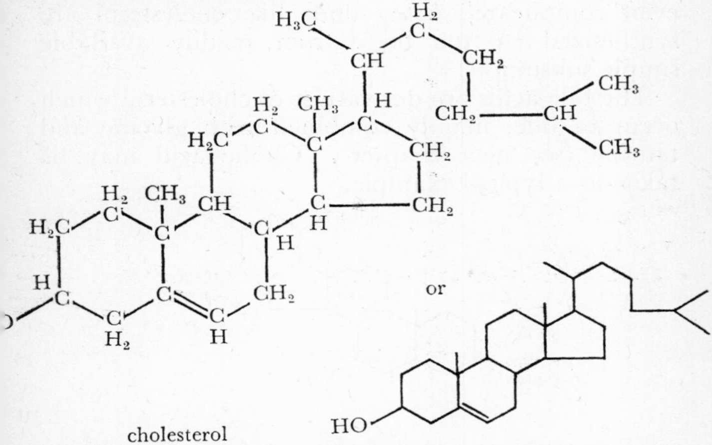

cholesterol

This compound which is the best known representative of the sterols occurs in all animal tissues (never in plants), and is particularly abundant in bile, blood, milk, egg yolk, brain tissue and the adrenal glands.

The commonest type of human gallstone is also composed mainly of cholesterol whereas the grease of skin, and ear wax are fatty acid esters of cholesterol.

Dehydrocholesterol (cholesterol with another double bond) is present in small amounts in the skin and is converted to vitamin D_3 by the action of ultra-violet light. This steroid vitamin prevents the formation of rickets which explains the beneficial action of sunshine against this deficiency disease.

Another member of the vitamin D group—calciferol (vitamin D_2) is formed in a similar way from ergosterol, found in ergot and yeast.

Other plant sterols include stigmasterol and sito-sterol.

It has now been shown by means of molecules containing radioactive or other isotopic atoms that even complicated compounds like cholesterol are synthesized by the body from readily available simple substances.

The bile acids are derivatives of cholesterol which occur in bile, mainly combined with glycine and taurine (see next chapter). Cholic acid may be taken as a typical example.

cholic acid

The bile salts are very effective detergents and help to emulsify lipids and promote their intestinal absorption.

The cardiac glycosides are a group of very complex steroids combined with sugars which often have a marked stimulatory action on heart muscle. The leaves of the foxglove, Digitalis, is a good source of these compounds.

Vitamin D and the sex and adrenocortical steroids are discussed later (see Chapters X and XI).

FAT METABOLISM

Fat digestion and absorption.

Fat, apart from acting as a heat insulator, is the most compact form of energy stored by the body.

It also gives rise to twice as much water on complete oxidation as does carbohydrate or protein and it is this " metabolic water " from fat that is of importance to those terrestrial animals that live or develop under conditions of acute water shortage.

Finally, fat forms an important part of the structure of living tissues. This is called the " constant element " as opposed to the " variable element " which varies in amount with the nutritional state of the animal.

After ingestion, fat is not attacked by fat-digesting enzymes (lipases) until it reaches the duodenum, i.e. the part of the intestine just below the stomach.

Conditions here are slightly acidic and favourable to the lipases secreted by the pancreas which remove fatty acid molecules one at a time from the fat (triglyceride), resulting in the formation of mono-, and diglycerides, glycerol and fatty acids.

Only 30 per cent of the fat is broken down in this manner; the rest is emulsified (i.e. dispersed into very small particles) and absorbed as neutral fat from the intestine. After a fatty meal, fat droplets of very small size—the chylomicrons, are always present in the blood.

Since fat is insoluble in water the emulsifying system which brings about this dispersion has been shown to be a mixture of fatty acid, monoglyceride and bile salts, all of which are normally present in the duodenum. This is the only system which is effective at the pH prevailing in that part of the intestine.

$$CH_2OOCR^1$$
$$|$$
$$CHOOCR^{11} \quad \xrightarrow[\text{lipase}]{\text{hydrolysis}}$$
$$|$$
$$CH_2OOCR^{111}$$
fat (triglyceride)

$$CH_2OH$$
$$|$$
$$CHOOCR^{11}$$
$$|$$
$$CH_2OOCR^{111}$$
diglyceride
$$+ R^1COOH$$
fatty acid
$$\downarrow \text{hydrolysis}$$

$$CH_2OH$$
$$|$$
$$CHOH \quad \xleftarrow[\substack{\text{hydrolysis} \\ \text{(slow)}}]{\text{further}}$$
$$|$$
$$CH_2OH$$
glycerol
$$+ R^{11}COOH$$
fatty acid

$$CH_2OH$$
$$|$$
$$CHOOCR^{11}$$
$$|$$
$$CH_2OH$$
monoglyceride
$$+ R^{111}COOH$$
fatty acid

Fat absorption is impaired in the absence of pancreatic juice or in obstructive jaundice when no bile can reach the intestine and, under these circumstances, large amounts of lipids appear in the faeces.

The dispersed fat particles pass through the cells of the intestinal wall and from there enter the lymphatic system, i.e. a system of vessels in the body carrying a fluid similar to blood plasma, which empties into the main vascular (blood-carrying) system. After a lipid-rich meal these channels are filled with a milky fluid, the chyle, containing the absorbed fat particles on their way to the blood. Most of the absorbed fat is then either oxidized in the liver or deposited in the fat depots of the body until required to provide energy.

Generally, the composition of the fat depots is characteristic of the species. However, not all fat in the body comes from dietary lipids and it is readily synthesized from carbohydrate or substances capable of forming carbohydrate. Thus, the hard fat of herbivores is derived almost exclusively from cellulose which is converted to short-chain fatty acids by the microorganisms inhabiting their alimentary tract.

The lipids in the depots are not inert metabolically and are replaced continuously even in well-fed animals.

The oxidation of fatty acids.

β-oxidation.

Fatty acids are broken down in stepwise manner with the removal of two carbon atoms at a time by the process of β-oxidation. The —CH_2— group in the position β to the carboxyl group is first oxidized to —CO— and the resulting compound then hydrolysed at that point.

$$CH_3—CH_2\ldots\ldots\ldots CH_2—CH_2—\underset{\beta}{CH_2}—\underset{\alpha}{CH_2}—COOH$$
$$\downarrow O_2$$
$$CH_3—CH_2\ldots\ldots\ldots CH_2—CH_2—CO—CH_2—COOH$$
$$\downarrow H_2O$$
$$CH_3—CH_2\ldots\ldots\ldots CH_2—\underset{\beta}{CH_2}—\underset{\alpha}{COOH} + {}^*CH_3COOH$$
$$\downarrow O_2$$
$$CH_3—CH_2\ldots\ldots\ldots CO—CH_2—COOH$$
$$\downarrow etc.$$

In this way even-numbered carbon atom fatty acids are completely broken down to acetic acid* which is then further oxidized by the citric acid cycle. All these reactions occur in the mitochondria and NAD is involved in the oxidation.

The synthesis of fat from active acetate* (see below)

---

* The compound formed is " active acetate " (see footnote in Chapter VII).

has many of the features of β-oxidation in reverse so that it is not surprising that most naturally-occurring fatty acids contain an even number of carbon atoms.

When fatty acids with an odd number of carbon atoms are fed, they give rise to propionic acid (CH_3CH_2COOH) which is converted to succinate and then either broken down in the citric acid cycle or else built up into glycogen.

The fact that β-oxidation is the main pathway of fatty acid degradation was discovered by Knoop. He was among the first to use labelled compounds (see Chapter II) to study metabolism and in his experiment he fed fatty acids containing a phenyl group to animals and then examined their urine for excretion products.

He found that no matter how many different phenyl labelled fatty acids were fed only two acids could be detected in the urine—benzoic and phenyl acetic acid, both conjugated with glycine (see Chapter III). The former was obtained from fatty acids with an odd number of carbon atoms and the latter from those with an even number of carbon atoms.

The only possible way to account for this is by β-oxidation.

1) Acid with even number of C atoms:

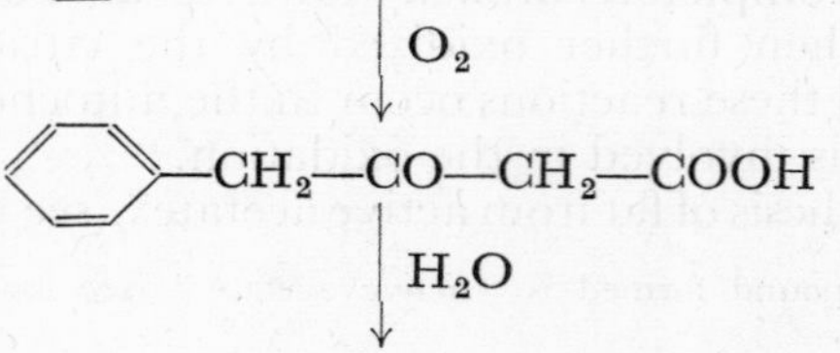

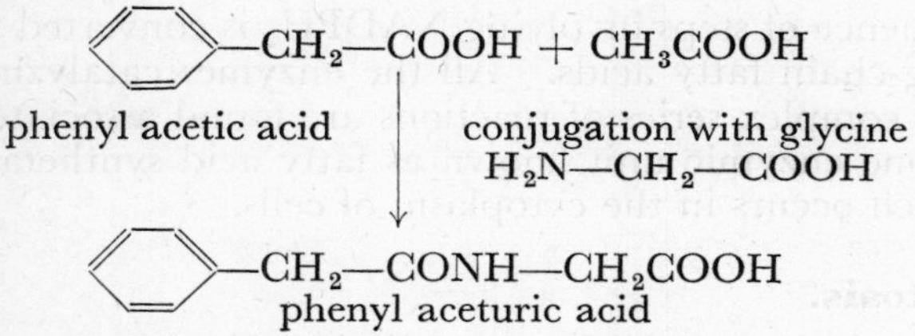

⬡—CH₂—COOH + CH₃COOH

phenyl acetic acid   conjugation with glycine
$H_2N—CH_2—COOH$

⬡—CH₂—CONH—CH₂COOH
phenyl aceturic acid

2) Acid with odd number of C atoms:

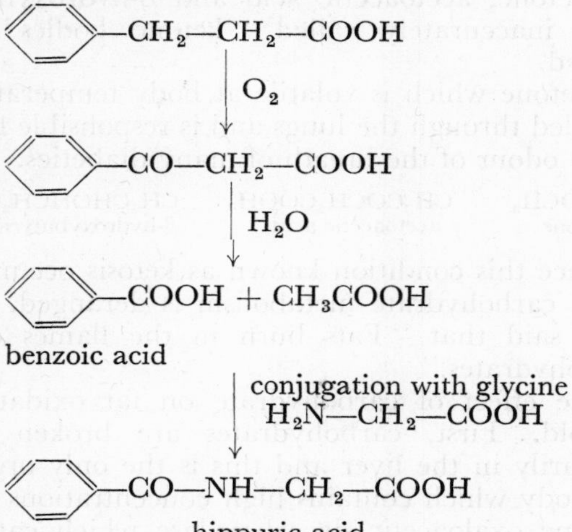

⬡—CH₂—CH₂—COOH

O_2

⬡—CO—CH₂—COOH

H_2O

⬡—COOH + CH₃COOH
benzoic acid

conjugation with glycine
$H_2N—CH_2—COOH$

⬡—CO—NH—CH₂—COOH
hippuric acid

Synthesis of fatty acids.

Although active acetate is the chief precursor of long-chain fatty acids and many of the reactions are like β-oxidation in reverse, there are a number of different steps, again illustrating the principle that synthesis differs at some point from the reverse of degradation.

Initially, active malonate* is formed which by a

* Coenzyme A derivative of malonic acid (HOOCCH₂COOH).

sequence of steps involving $NADPH_2$ is converted to long-chain fatty acids. All the enzymes catalyzing this complex series of reactions are found associated in one enzymic unit known as fatty acid synthetase which occurs in the cytoplasm of cells.

Ketosis.

During starvation or sugar diabetes large amounts of acetone, acetoacetic acid and β-hydroxybutyric acid, inaccurately called "ketone bodies", are formed.

Acetone which is volatile at body temperature is expelled through the lungs and is responsible for the fruity odour of the breath of many diabetics.

CH_3COCH_3	CH_3COCH_2COOH	$CH_3CHOHCH_2COOH$
acetone	acetoacetic acid	β-hydroxybutyric acid

Since this condition known as ketosis occurs only when carbohydrate metabolism is deranged, it has been said that "Fats burn in the flames of the carbohydrates."

The effect of carbohydrate on fat oxidation is twofold. First, carbohydrates are broken down primarily in the liver and this is the only organ in the body which contains high concentrations of the enzyme oxaloacetic decarboxylase which catalyzes the following reversible reaction:

$$
\begin{array}{c}
CH_3 \\
| \\
CO \\
| \\
COOH
\end{array}
+ CO_2
\underset{\text{decarboxylase}}{\overset{\text{oxaloacetic}}{\rightleftharpoons}}
\begin{array}{c}
COOH \\
| \\
CH_2 \\
| \\
CO \\
| \\
COOH
\end{array}
$$

pyruvic acid   oxaloacetic acid

The equilibrium position lies very much to the

left so that unless large amounts of pyruvate are formed from its main source—carbohydrate—not enough oxaloacetate will be produced for the citric acid cycle to operate at full capacity. This will result in active acetate accumulating instead of being fully oxidized to carbon dioxide and water.

Second, in the absence of carbohydrate metabolism abnormally large amounts of fat will be oxidized to provide energy resulting in even more active acetate being formed. The accumulated acetate molecules then react with each other to form aceto-acetate. Some of this product is either reduced to β-hydroxybutyric acid or else decarboxylated, i.e. carbon dioxide eliminated from the molecule, to form acetone:

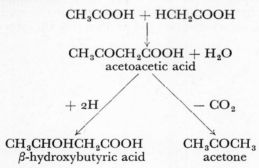

$$CH_3COOH + HCH_2COOH$$

$$CH_3COCH_2COOH + H_2O$$
acetoacetic acid

$$+ 2H \qquad\qquad - CO_2$$

$$CH_3CHOHCH_2COOH \qquad CH_3COCH_3$$
β-hydroxybutyric acid   acetone

In starvation, ketosis occurs as a result of the rapid depletion of the carbohydrate reserves followed by excessive breakdown of fat, whereas, in sugar diabetes, ketosis is partly due to a defect in carbohydrate utilization. Mild ketosis may also occur after a very fatty meal when the citric acid cycle becomes overloaded with acetate and is unable to oxidize it all. Eskimoes, however, whose diet is extremely rich in fat, seem to manage quite well.

Fatty liver.

The main site of fat degradation and synthesis is the liver and, under normal conditions any fat conveyed to it from the depots is oxidized and does not accumulate in this organ. Under certain circumstances however, the fat content of the liver may rise considerably and result in the condition known as fatty liver. Of special interest in this connection was the discovery by Best in Toronto that small amounts of choline given in the diet could prevent this condition.

Subsequent studies showed that methionine or protein rich in this amino acid (see next chapter) also had a lipotropic action, i.e. prevented the fatty infiltration of the liver—and that this compound acted by providing methyl groups for the synthesis of choline, a constituent of lecithin (see Chapter IX).

CHAPTER IX

PROTEINS AND NUCLEIC ACIDS

The nature of proteins.

PROTEINS are very complex organic compounds containing the elements carbon, hydrogen, oxygen, nitrogen, sulphur and sometimes other elements. On hydrolysis they yield many different amino acids (see later section) and, in fact, all proteins are made up from these units.

Protein is invariably associated with living matter being one of the essential constituents of protoplasm and all enzymes and several hormones (see Chapter XI) belong to this group of compounds.

Protein is indispensable in the diet and can be converted to both carbohydrate and fat in the body. Typical examples are provided by the albumin of egg white, casein of milk, globin of haemoglobin or the keratin of skin and hair.

The physical and chemical properties of proteins are the same as those described for the enzymes (see Chapter IV) and they may be divided into two main groups:

1) Simple proteins.
2) Conjugated proteins.

The former on hydrolysis yield only amino acids whereas the latter are combined (conjugated) with other groups which may be:

a) Phosphate—in the phosphoproteins.
b) Nucleic acid—in the nucleoproteins.

c) Carbohydrate—in the glycoproteins.
d) Lipids—in the lipoproteins.
e) Haem, riboflavin or other compounds.

The different simple proteins differ from each other in their molecular size, the percentage of each particular amino present and also in the sequence and arrangement of these amino acids, with the result that their complexity has so far defied complete analysis with certain notable exceptions. These include insulin, haemoglobin, cytochrome and the enzyme ribonuclease. However, although the sequence of amino acids in these few proteins is known, there is very much less information available about the manner in which they are folded and arranged in three-dimensions. These factors are important for the protein to show full biological activity.

The plasma proteins.

The proteins of blood plasma are synthesized mainly in the liver and act as a reserve. In starvation their concentration may be lowered considerably and, since they exert osmotic pressure (see Chapter II), a characteristic symptom is oedema, i.e. swelling of the tissues due to the influx of fluid from the blood into them.

Two main groups of proteins are present in serum—the albumins and globulins while plasma, in addition, contains fibrinogen and prothrombin, both for the clotting of blood.

Blood clotting.

When bleeding occurs as a result of injury to a blood vessel, a clot is formed by the healthy normal animal to prevent any further loss of blood.

This coagulation however is the result of a very complicated sequence of events and it is also interesting to consider why the blood circulating in the body does not do this.

Blood contains in addition to white and red cells, special cells called platelets which release an enzyme —thrombokinase—whenever a wound is produced and they are damaged. This compound in the presence of calcium ions catalyzes the conversion of inactive prothrombin into the active enzyme thrombin which in turn converts the soluble protein fibrinogen into fibrin. The latter compound is an insoluble fibrous protein which forms a sticky jelly and solidifies into the familiar blood clot.

Prevention of clotting can be achieved by the addition of oxalate or citrate, heparin, hirudin or cobra venom.

The first two of these compounds act by precipitating inorganic calcium which is essential for the conversion of prothrombin into thrombin by thrombokinase, and heparin also prevents the formation of thrombin, but in a different manner. Heparin is a normal constituent of blood and prevents the formation of clots inside the blood vessels. However, after an operation it may be unable to prevent this and an internal clot or thrombus may form resulting in thrombosis. Although the clot usually retracts towards the walls of the blood vessels, in some cases it may either block it or become detached and lodge itself in some vital area such as the heart, lung or brain. Such a detached thrombus is called an embolus and embolism may be fatal or cause permanent paralysis. Heparin or other anticoagulating agents are often injected before an operation or blood transfusion.

In haemophilia, which is a rare hereditary disease

occurring in males but transmitted by the female, there is a defect in the conversion of prothrombin to thrombin due to the absence of antihaemophilic globulin in the plasma.

Cobra venom and hirudin from the salivary glands of the leech and other blood sucking animals act in a different way by inhibiting the activity of thrombin rather than its formation. Normal blood also contains an antithrombin which destroys thrombin which explains why blood does not clot immediately. This can only occur when the concentration of thrombin has become large enough to be in excess of the amount destroyed.

In the laboratory, a convenient way to prevent fresh blood from clotting is to remove the fibrinogen by rapidly stirring with a glass rod so that all the fibrin adheres to it.

Menstrual blood contains neither fibrinogen nor prothrombin and will therefore not coagulate.

Finally, vitamin K (see Chapter X) is essential for the synthesis of prothrombin and a deficiency of this vitamin leads to haemorrhage due to impairment of the blood clotting mechanism.

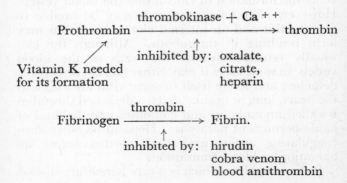

Protein digestion.

The digestion of protein takes place in the stomach and small intestine and results in its complete degradation to amino acids. These relatively simple compounds are then readily absorbed through the intestinal wall.

a) Gastric digestion.

Two proteolytic (protein-digesting) enzymes, pepsin and rennin, are present in the stomach, although the latter occurs only in suckling mammals and is practically non-existent in the adult. Both are secreted as inactive proenzymes—pepsinogen and prorennin, but are converted to the active form by the hydrochloric acid of the stomach.

Pepsin is autocatalytic being able to convert pepsinogen to pepsin so that once a small amount of it has been formed, it catalyzes its own activation.

Pepsin breaks down food proteins to small polypeptides which are still fairly complex compounds, made up of many amino acids while rennin acts primarily on casein—the phosphoprotein of milk. This compound is converted to paracasein which combines with calcium ions in the stomach to form a curd and since the new born mammal lives solely on milk, it is quite evident why rennin should be present at this stage of life.

Rennet used in making junket and cheese is a commercial preparation of rennin.

b) Intestinal digestion.

The proteolytic enzymes may be divided into two main groups: 1) The endopeptidases which like pepsin attack the protein near the middle as well as at the end of the molecule, liberating different sizes of protein fragments.

I

2) The exopeptidases which attack only the terminal parts of the protein or protein fragment thus liberating mainly amino acids. In both cases however the points of hydrolytic attack are the peptide linkages.

$$R{-}CO{-}NH{-}R' \xrightarrow[\text{proteolytic enzyme}]{H_2O} RCOOH + H_2N{-}R'$$

As mentioned earlier (see Chapter IV), the proteolytic enzymes are fairly selective and the nature of the amino acid R and R' are both important in determining whether a particular peptide bond is hydrolyzed.

The intestinal endopeptidases.

Like pepsin the two intestinal endopeptidases are secreted in their inactive forms: trypsinogen and chymotrypsinogen. The former is converted by enterokinase an enzyme present in intestinal secretion to trypsin which then acts autocatalytically converting more trypsinogen to its active form.

Enterokinase, however, has no action on chymotrypsinogen which is converted to chymotrypsin by trypsin. Chymotrypsin does not behave autocatalytically. Thus, once enterokinase has liberated a small amount of trypsin, no other enzymes are needed to activate the endopeptidases.

$$\text{trypsinogen} \xrightarrow{\text{enterokinase}} \text{trypsin}$$

$$\text{trypsinogen} \xrightarrow{\text{trypsin}} \text{trypsin}$$

$$\text{chymotrypsinogen} \xrightarrow{\text{trypsin}} \text{chymotrypsin}$$

The intestinal exopeptidases.

Formerly known collectively as erepsin, these digestive enzymes have now been grouped into: *a*) carboxypeptidases, *b*) aminopeptidases, and *c*) dipeptidases.

Being exopeptidases they only attack terminal peptide groups but whereas the carboxypeptidases remove amino acids with a free carboxyl group, the aminopeptidases require a free amino group. Dipeptidases attack only dipeptides, i.e. peptides composed of two amino acids.

$$\underset{\text{amino peptidase}}{H_2N-CH-CO\overset{R'}{\underset{|}{}}} \quad NH-CH-CO \quad NH-CH-COOH$$

a protein fragment

All the proteolytic enzymes described so far are liberated into the alimentary canal in the gastric and intestinal juices and are therefore extracellular enzymes, but others remain inside the cell and carry out their functions there. The intracellular enzymes of animals are known as cathepsins and some correspond to pepsin or trypsin, while others to the other proteolytic enzymes mentioned.

In very primitive animals all digestion is intracellular. In plants three such enzymes are ficin from the fig, bromelin from the pineapple and papain from the papaya (paw-paw)—an edible fruit found in Africa and America.

The amino acids.

Proteins on complete hydrolysis yield about 20 different amino acids, all of which possess the following characteristic structure:

$$\begin{array}{c} H \\ | \\ R-C_{\alpha}-COOH \\ | \\ NH_2 \end{array}$$

They have a carboxyl and an amino group on the α-carbon atom and they all have rather similar physical and chemical properties. Most of them are very water-soluble, all have been obtained in crystalline form and, with the exception of glycine, they are all optically active because they have an asymmetric carbon atom. (See Chapter VI).

Some amino acids can be readily synthesized in the body and their presence in food is therefore not essential, whereas others, called essential amino acids, cannot be formed by the tissues and must be provided in the diet.

When protein is given to a diabetic animal, an increased output of glucose or " ketone bodies " is observed showing that some of the amino acids have been converted into these metabolites. Those amino acids which give rise to carbohydrate under these conditions are glycogenic whereas those which increase the output of " ketone bodies " are said to be ketogenic.

Some of the more important amino acids are:

Glycine.

$$\begin{array}{c} H \\ | \\ H-C-COOH \\ | \\ NH_2 \end{array}$$

Glycine is the simplest amino acid and is the only member of the group that is not optically active. It is glycogenic, non-essential and has a sweetish taste in solution.

It is widely used by the body to build more complex molecules and when this amino acid is labelled with isotopic atoms and fed to animals the "label" is found in many important biological compounds. These include glucose, haem, uric acid (see below), creatine and the amino acids serine, sarcosine and alanine.

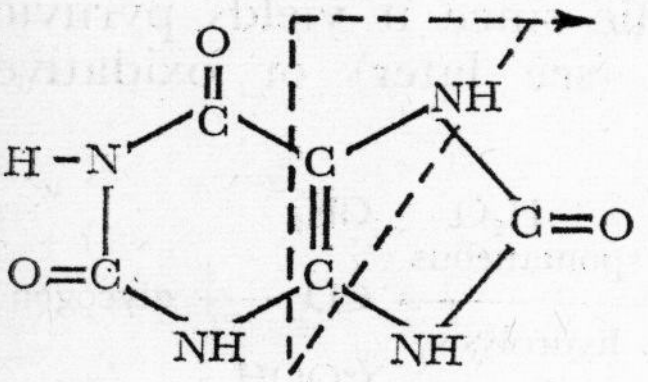

derived from glycine

uric acid

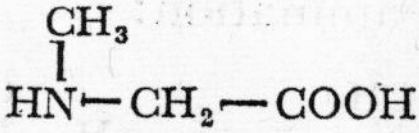

sarcosine (methyl glycine)

The tripeptide glutathione, which is a reducing agent (see Chapter V) present in many tissues, also contains glycine.

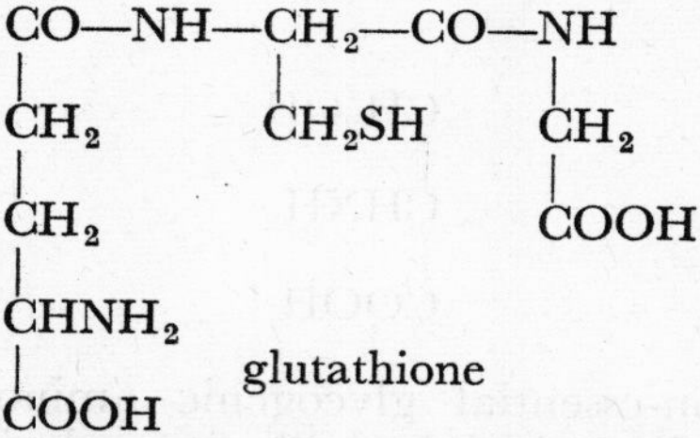

glutathione

(glutamyl—cysteinyl—glycine)

Glycine is also important in detoxication reactions (see Chapter III), and is found combined with cholic acid in the bile salt, sodium glycocholate (see Chapter VIII).

Alanine.

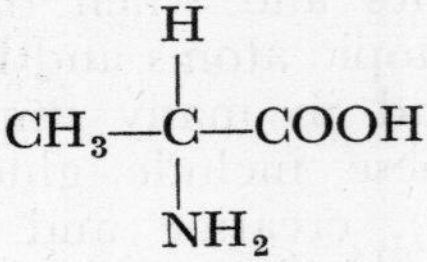

$$CH_3-\underset{\underset{NH_2}{|}}{\overset{\overset{H}{|}}{C}}-COOH$$

The next simplest amino acid, alanine, is non-essential and is glycogenic since it yields pyruvic acid on transamination (see later) or oxidative deamination:

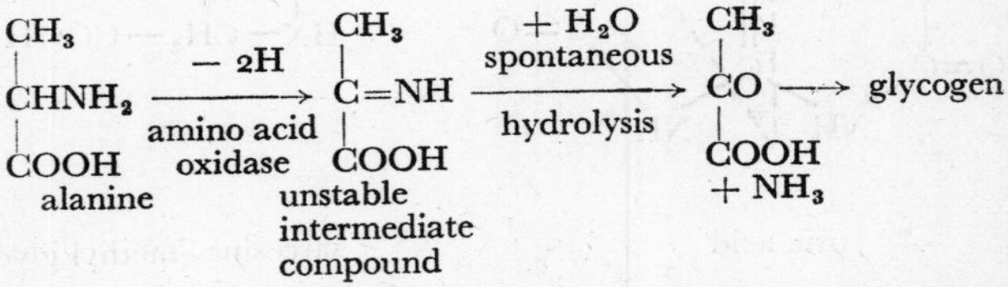

$$\underset{\substack{alanine}}{\overset{CH_3}{\underset{COOH}{\overset{|}{\underset{|}{CHNH_2}}}}} \xrightarrow[\substack{amino\ acid \\ oxidase}]{-\ 2H} \underset{\substack{unstable \\ intermediate \\ compound}}{\overset{CH_3}{\underset{COOH}{\overset{|}{\underset{|}{C=NH}}}}} \xrightarrow[\substack{hydrolysis}]{\substack{+\ H_2O \\ spontaneous}} \underset{\substack{+\ NH_3}}{\overset{CH_3}{\underset{COOH}{\overset{|}{\underset{|}{CO}}}}} \longrightarrow glycogen$$

Pyruvic acid need not necessarily be built up to glycogen but if it is oxidized then an equivalent amount of carbohydrate will be spared.

Serine.

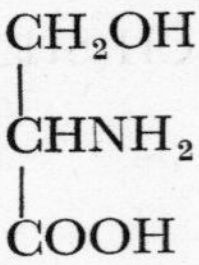

$$\underset{COOH}{\overset{CH_2OH}{\underset{|}{\overset{|}{\underset{|}{CHNH_2}}}}}$$

This non-essential glycogenic amino acid can be readily formed in the body from glycine.

It gives rise to ethanolamine on decarboxylation, while on methylation it is converted to choline found in many phospholipids. Choline in turn can give rise to acetylcholine, the transmitter substance of nerve endings.

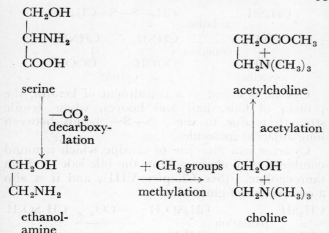

CH₂OH
|
CHNH₂
|
COOH

serine

$$\downarrow \quad \begin{array}{c} -CO_2 \\ \text{decarboxy-} \\ \text{lation} \end{array}$$

CH₂OH
|
CH₂NH₂

ethanol-
amine

+ CH₃ groups
—————————→
methylation

CH₂OCOCH₃
| +
CH₂N(CH₃)₃

acetylcholine

↑ acetylation

CH₂OH
| +
CH₂N(CH₃)₃

choline

Serine is also able to exchange its —OH group with an —SH group in the body thus forming the amino acid, cysteine (see below). This reaction, however, involves the essential amino acid, methionine, so that unless the latter is present, cysteine cannot be made from serine and thus becomes an essential amino acid which must be provided in the diet.

Cysteine.

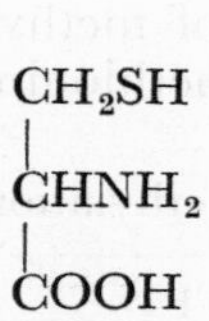

CH₂SH
|
CHNH₂
|
COOH

Cysteine and its oxidation product, cystine, are the commonest sulphur-containing amino acids and, together with methionine (see below), they are the chief source of sulphur in the diet.

$$\begin{array}{ccc}
\text{CH}_2\text{SH} & & \text{CH}_2\text{—S—S—CH}_2 \\
| & \text{oxidation} & | \qquad | \\
2 \quad \text{CHNH}_2 & \rightleftharpoons & \text{CHNH}_2 \qquad \text{CHNH}_2 \\
| & \text{reduction} & | \qquad | \\
\text{COOH} & & \text{COOH} \qquad \text{COOH} \\
\text{cysteine} & & \text{cystine}
\end{array}$$

Cystine is found as a constituent of keratin, the protein of hair, nail and hooves, whose tensile strength is due to the —S—S— bonds between long adjacent molecules.

Cysteine can give rise to taurine which is found combined with cholic acid in the bile salt—sodium taurocholate. (See Chapter VIII), and it is also a component of glutathione.

$$\begin{array}{ccccc}
\text{CH}_2\text{SH} & & \text{CH}_2\text{SO}_3\text{H} & \text{—CO}_2 & \text{CH}_2\text{SO}_3\text{H} \\
| & \text{oxidation} & | & \xrightarrow{\hspace{1cm}} & | \\
\text{CHNH}_2 & \xrightarrow{\hspace{1cm}} & \text{CHNH}_2 & \text{decarboxyl-} & \text{CH}_2\text{NH}_2 \\
| & & | & \text{ation} & \\
\text{COOH} & & \text{COOH} & & \\
\text{cysteine} & & \text{cysteic acid} & & \text{taurine}
\end{array}$$

In cystinuria, a rare inborn error of metabolism, large quantities of cystine are eliminated in the urine and may result in the formation of cystine stones (calculi).

The other main sulphur-containing amino acid, methionine, is involved in transmethylation reactions. The transfer of methyl groups requires the initial activation of methionine by ATP.

$$\begin{array}{ccccc}
\text{S—CH}_3 & & & \text{SH} & \\
| & \text{transmethylation} & & | & \\
(\text{CH}_2)_2 & + \text{RH} \xrightarrow{\hspace{1.5cm}} & & (\text{CH}_2)_2 & + \text{R—CH}_3 \\
| & \text{ATP} & & | & \\
\text{CHNH}_2 & & & \text{CHNH}_2 & \\
| & & & | & \\
\text{COOH} & & & \text{COOH} & \\
\text{methi-} \quad \text{acceptor} & & & \text{homocysteine} & \text{methylated} \\
\text{onine} \quad \text{compound} & & & & \text{compound}
\end{array}$$

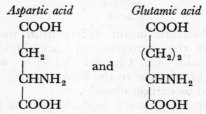

Phenylalanine

NH₂

CH₂CHCOOH

and

Tyrosine

NH₂

CH₂CHCOOH

OH

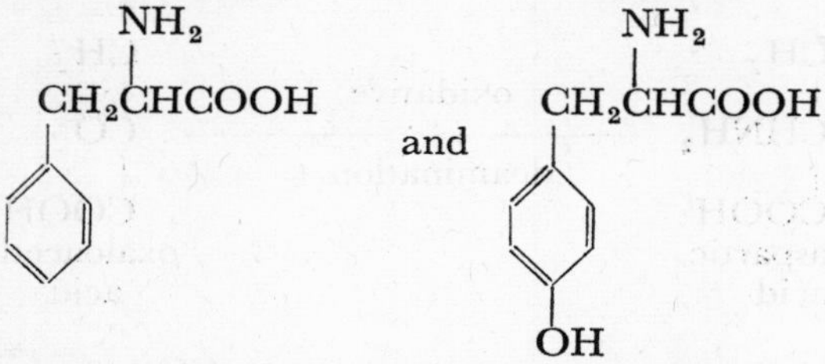

Phenylalanine is a ketogenic essential amino acid which gives rise to tyrosine and also to the hormones, adrenaline and thyroxine (see Chapter XI). Tyrosine is readily oxidized by tyrosinase to melanin, the brown pigment of hair and skin.

Aspartic acid

COOH

CH₂

CHNH₂

COOH

and

Glutamic acid

COOH

(CH₂)₂

CHNH₂

COOH

The amino acids mentioned so far have all had one carboxyl and one amino group (neutral amino acids), but aspartic acid and its next higher homologue, glutamic acid, possess two acidic carboxyl groups to one basic amino group and are therefore acidic.

They are both non-essential, and glycogenic because they yield citric acid cycle intermediates on oxidative deamination. Thus aspartic acid gives rise to oxaloacetate, and glutamic acid to α-ketoglutarate. Oxaloacetate is decarboxylated in the liver to pyruvate which can then give rise to glucose or glycogen.

$$
\begin{array}{c}
\text{COOH} \\
|\\
\text{CH}_2 \\
|\\
\text{CHNH}_2 \\
|\\
\text{COOH}
\end{array}
\xrightarrow[\text{deamination}]{\text{oxidative}}
\begin{array}{c}
\text{COOH} \\
|\\
\text{CH}_2 \\
|\\
\text{CO} \\
|\\
\text{COOH}
\end{array}
$$

aspartic acid   oxaloacetic acid

$-CO_2$
β-decarboxylation

$$
\begin{array}{c}
\text{CH}_3 \\
|\\
\text{CO} \\
|\\
\text{COOH}
\end{array}
$$

glucose or glycogen ← pyruvic acid

This decarboxylation differs from the one involved in the formation of acetaldehyde from pyruvic acid (see Chapter VII) in which the carboxyl group next to the keto group ($-C=O$) is eliminated as carbon dioxide.

Aspartic and glutamic acid also play an important role in transamination, i.e. the transference of an amino group from one amino acid to an α-keto acid such as pyruvic acid for instance with the formation of another amino acid.

$$
\begin{array}{c}
\text{COOH} \\
|\\
\text{CH}_2 \\
|\\
\text{CHNH}_2 \\
|\\
\text{COOH}
\end{array}
+
\begin{array}{c}
\text{CH}_3 \\
|\\
\text{CO} \\
|\\
\text{COOH}
\end{array}
\xrightarrow[\text{transaminase}]{\text{aspartic}}
\begin{array}{c}
\text{COOH} \\
|\\
\text{CH}_2 \\
|\\
\text{CO} \\
|\\
\text{COOH}
\end{array}
+
\begin{array}{c}
\text{CH}_3 \\
|\\
\text{CHNH}_2 \\
|\\
\text{COOH}
\end{array}
$$

aspartic acid   pyruvic acid   oxaloacetic acid   alanine

Both glutamic and aspartic acid play a part in the storage of ammonia by combining with it to form glutamine and asparagine respectively. This reaction requires energy which, as usual, is provided by ATP.

$$
\begin{array}{ccc}
\begin{array}{l}
\text{COOH} \\
| \\
\text{CH}_2 \\
| \\
\text{CH}_2 \\
| \\
\text{CHNH}_2 \\
| \\
\text{COOH} \\
\text{glutamic} \\
\text{acid}
\end{array}
& + \text{NH}_3 \underset{\longleftarrow}{\overset{\text{ATP}}{\rightleftharpoons}} &
\begin{array}{l}
\text{CONH}_2 \\
| \\
\text{CH}_2 \\
| \\
\text{CH}_2 \\
| \\
\text{CHNH}_2 \\
| \\
\text{COOH} \\
\text{glutamine}
\end{array}
& + \text{H}_2\text{O}
\end{array}
$$

When ammonia is needed to neutralize acids, these two compounds liberate it and are converted back to amino acids in the process. Ammonia formation from glutamine in the kidneys is an important mechanism for the conservation of body sodium and potassium.

$$
\begin{array}{cc}
\textit{Ornithine} & \textit{Lysine} \\
\begin{array}{l}
\text{NH}_2 \\
| \\
(\text{CH}_2)_3 \\
| \\
\text{CHNH}_2 \\
| \\
\text{COOH}
\end{array}
& \text{and}
\begin{array}{l}
\text{NH}_2 \\
| \\
(\text{CH}_2)_4 \\
| \\
\text{CHNH}_2 \\
| \\
\text{COOH}
\end{array}
\end{array}
$$

Examples of basic amino acids, i.e. having amino groups in excess of carboxyl groups are provided by ornithine and lysine, the latter being essential in the diet.

They are decarboxylated by intestinal bacteria to putrescine and cadaverine respectively, and these amines, which are also found in putrefying flesh, were once thought to be responsible for " ptomaine " poisoning. However, it is now known that they have only low toxicity.

$$NH_2$$
$(CH_2)_3$ putrescine $\qquad$ $(CH_2)_4$ cadaverine
$$CH_2NH_2 \qquad\qquad\qquad CH_2NH_2$$

Tryptophan.

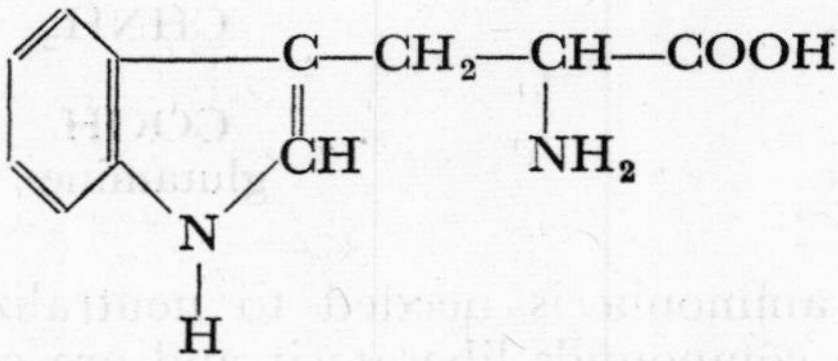

This rather unusual amino acid is essential though whether it is glycogenic or ketogenic is not known. It is converted by intestinal bacteria to indole and skatole, which contribute to the unpleasant odour of faeces.

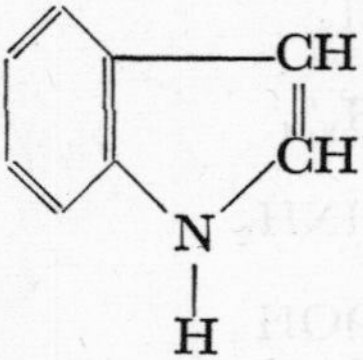

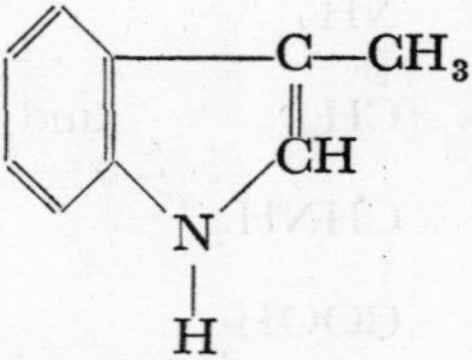

Another intestinal degradation product of trytophan, indole acetic acid, promotes plant growth, while serotonin (5-hydroxytryptamine) increases blood pressure and also intestinal movement (peristalsis) by its action on smooth muscle.

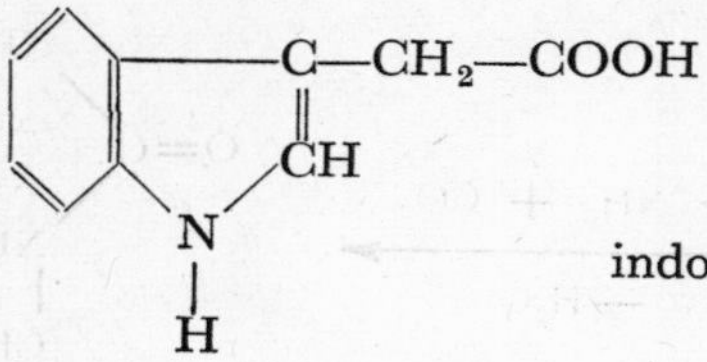

$$C—CH_2—COOH$$

$$CH$$

$$N$$
$$H$$

indole acetic acid

Histidine.

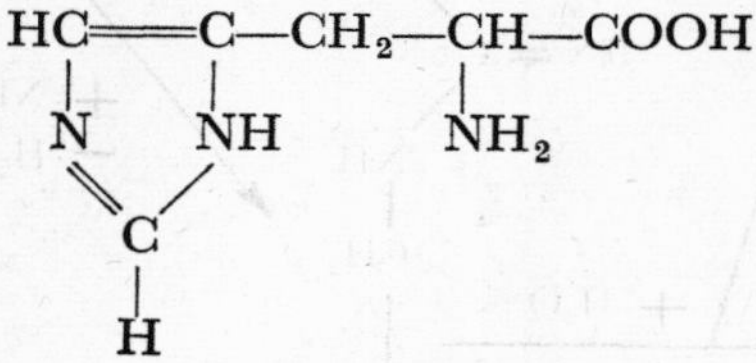

$$HC \!=\!\!=\! C—CH_2—CH—COOH$$

$$N \quad NH \quad NH_2$$

$$C$$

$$H$$

This essential amino acid on decarboxylation gives rise to histamine which can cause a marked lowering of blood pressure and other symptoms of shock. Histamine is also liberated during allergic reactions and it stimulates the secretion of both pepsin and acid by the stomach.

Formation of urea.

The ammonia produced on deamination of amino acids is very poisonous and in mammals is rendered harmless by conversion to urea which is then eliminated in the urine.

The formation of urea occurs only in the liver and is a complex cyclical process. The scheme, which was first proposed by Krebs, involves the participation of the amino acids, ornithine, citrulline and arginine, and is known as the ornithine cycle.

$$
\begin{array}{c}
NH_2 \\
| \\
(CH_2)_3 \\
| \\
CH\,NH_2 \\
| \\
COOH \\
\text{ornithine}
\end{array}
\quad
\xrightarrow[\;-H_2O\;]{+\;NH_3\;+\;CO_2}
\quad
\begin{array}{c}
NH_2 \\
| \\
O{=}C \\
| \\
NH \\
| \\
(CH_2)_3 \\
| \\
CH.NH_2 \\
| \\
COOH \\
\text{citrulline}
\end{array}
$$

$$
HN{=}C
\begin{array}{c}
NH_2 \\
\\
NH \\
| \\
(CH_2)_3 \\
| \\
CH.NH_2 \\
| \\
COOH \\
\text{arginine}
\end{array}
\qquad
\begin{array}{c}
+\;NH_3 \\
-\;H_2O
\end{array}
$$

$$
\begin{array}{c}
NH_2 \\
| \\
C{=}O \\
| \\
NH_2 \\
\text{urea}
\end{array}
\quad
\xleftarrow{\;+\;H_2O\;}
\quad
\text{arginase}
$$

The ornithine cycle

This cycle does not occur in birds and reptiles where another compound, uric acid, is the main excretion product formed from ammonia.

The nucleic acids.

These substances, which are universally present in living cells, have attracted much interest because of their role in the transmission of hereditary characters and in the biosynthesis of proteins. They are present in the chromosomes of cell nuclei and also in the cytoplasm and consist of threadlike particles of high molecular weight. On hydrolysis, they yield a mixture of nitrogenous bases—the purines and pyrimidines, a pentose sugar (ribose or deoxyribose), and phosphoric acid.

The commonest pyrimidine constituents of nucleic acids are uracil, thymine and cytosine while the corresponding purines are adenine and guanine.

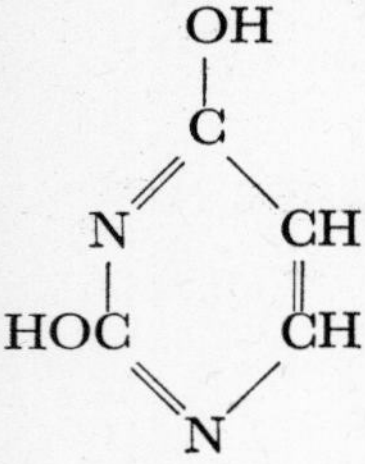

uracil 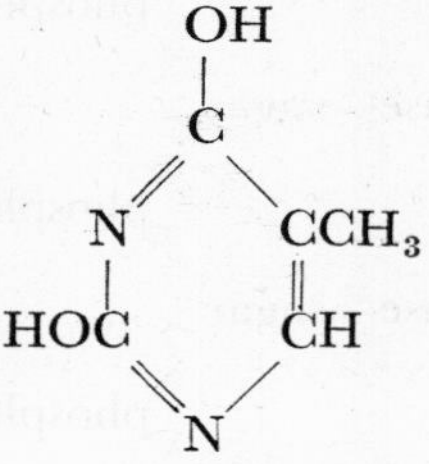   thymine 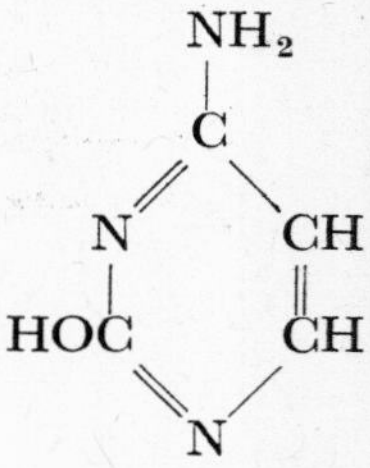   cytosine

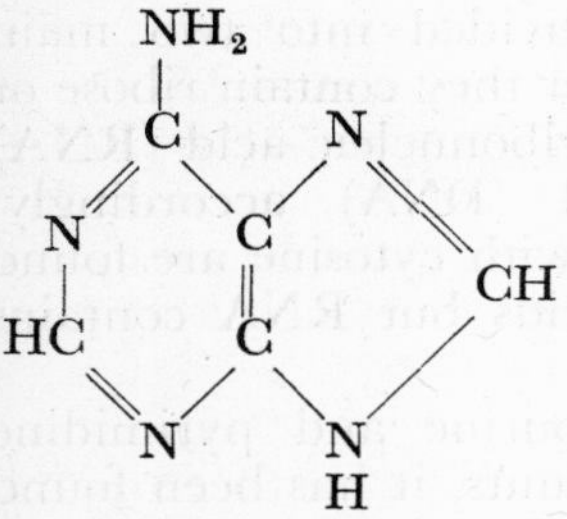

adenine 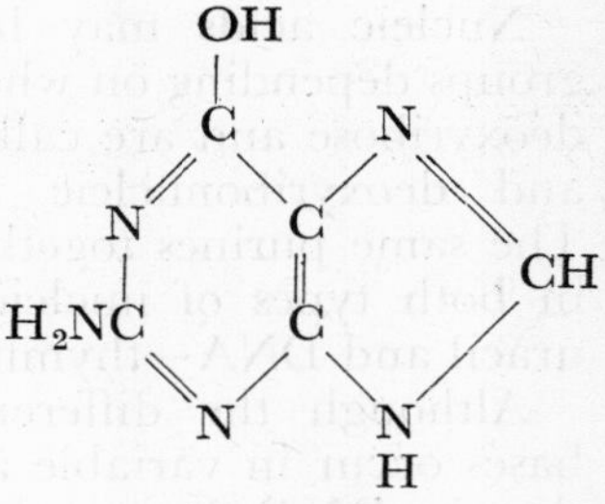   guanine

A purine or a pyrimidine combined with a pentose molecule esterified with phosphoric acid is known as a nucleotide. They form the structural units of nucleic acids in the same way that the amino acids form the fundamental building blocks of proteins. The nucleic acids are therefore poly-nucleotides and they are linked together by phosphate groups between sugar molecules:

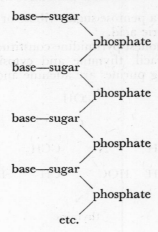

Nucleic acids may be divided into two main groups depending on whether they contain ribose or deoxyribose and are called ribonucleic acid (RNA) and deoxyribonucleic acid (DNA) accordingly. The same purines together with cytosine are found in both types of nucleic acids but RNA contains uracil and DNA—thymine.

Although the different purine and pyrimidine bases occur in variable amounts, it has been found that in DNA the number of purine nucleotides is equal to the number of pyrimidine nucleotides and that the ratio of adenine (A) to thymine (T), and of guanine (G) to cytosine (C) is 1. This and other evidence led Watson and Crick to propose that the DNA molecule consists of two complementary poly-nucleotide strands coiled in the form of a double helix with each adenine molecule lined up against a thymine molecule, and guanine against cytosine as shown diagrammatically:

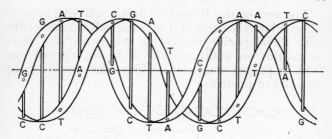

Very much less is known about the structure of RNA which is believed to consist of long fibres with small helical regions involving about half of its nucleotides. Three different types of RNA with different biochemical functions (see below) are known.

Protein synthesis.

Both DNA and RNA are now known to be intimately involved in the synthesis of protein which occurs on the ribosomes of the endoplasmic reticulum of the cell (see Chapter II).

First, each amino acid is activated by a reaction involving ATP and a specific enzyme, and the products are then bound selectively to a low molecular weight RNA known as soluble or transfer RNA (tRNA). These RNA-associated amino acid molecules now find their way to the ribosomes where the amino acids interact in peptide linkage to form specific proteins. This last reaction is directed by another type of RNA with only a short survival time, known as messenger RNA (mRNA) which can form complementary structures with DNA and diffuse out of the nucleus through pores in the membrane, thus conveying genetic information to the sites of protein synthesis.

K

The rest of the ribosomal RNA (rRNA) appears to be relatively inert and it is the mRNA molecules with their specific nucleotide sequences that serve as moulds on which amino acids are aligned and held in proper sequence to form the specific polypeptides of proteins.

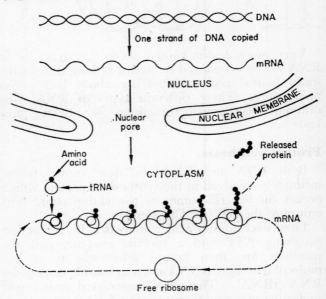

The synthesis of proteins in the cell

Groups of three bases in mRNA and hence also in DNA are needed to code each amino acid, and the RNA code sequence for all the amino acids commonly found in proteins has now been determined. It seems that the code must be " read " from a fixed starting point and, if this is displaced by even one base, the triplets are grouped incorrectly and yield either the wrong sequence of amino acids in the protein or no protein at all.

Peptide bond formation proceeds much like a zipper, starting with the amino acid at one end of a chain and closing bond after bond until the full protein molecule has been synthesized.

In the case of haemoglobin, new amino acids are added to the growing chains at the rate of about two per second and during this process the ribosomes move along the strand of mRNA and are eventually released.

Thus, the " one-gene—one enzyme " theory of Beadle, according to which each gene of the chromosomes is responsible for the production of a specific protein, has been borne out.

It is now possible to understand how protein (or enzyme) synthesis, and therefore all biochemical reactions, can be controlled at the genetic level. By activating or deactivating certain regions of the DNA molecule, the synthesis of any enzyme can be turned on or off and this type of regulation which is of primary importance during development and growth was first proposed by Jacob and Monod at the Pasteur Institute in Paris.

CHAPTER X

THE VITAMINS

VITAMINS are organic compounds that cannot be made in the body and must therefore be supplied in small amounts in the diet. They are essential for normal cellular function and deficiency diseases will develop in their absence even when adequate quantities of carbohydrate, fat and protein are provided.

The word " vitamine " (life-amine) was coined by Funk in 1911 when he isolated a basic organic compound—an amine—from rice husks, capable of preventing the disease beriberi. Later, however, it was shown that not all these substances are amines and the letter " e " was dropped from the original word. A good alternative name is accessory food factor.

Since organisms differ in their synthetic abilities, a substance that is a vitamin for one species may not be so for another. Thus, vitamin C must be provided in the diet of man, apes and guinea pigs but can be manufactured by all other animal species.

Many vitamins have now been discovered and they may be divided into two main groups depending on whether they are fat-soluble (vitamins A, D, E and K) or else water-soluble (all the other vitamins).

VITAMIN A

This vitamin is provided in an ordinary diet by liver, egg yolk, butter and some vegetables such as parsley, spinach and carrot.

$$CH_3 \quad CH_3$$
$$\underset{\displaystyle \overset{|}{C}}{} \qquad \qquad CH_3 \qquad\qquad\qquad CH_3$$

H₂C   C—CH=CH—C=CH—CH=CHC=CHCH₂OH

H₂C   CCH₃   Vitamin A

CH₂

Very much larger amounts are present in cod liver, shark liver and halibut liver* oils which are the sources used for the treatment of vitamin A deficiency.

A group of plant pigments, the carotenes, act as provitamins since they are readily converted to vitamin A in the body and therefore, although this vitamin is found in animals only, it is derived indirectly from the vegetable kingdom. Thus, the fishes mentioned above acquire their vitamin A by eating small crustaceans and smaller fishes, which in turn feed on minute plant organisms (algae etc.) rich in carotenoids.

However, not all carotenes act as provitamins and lycopene, the red carotenoid pigment of tomatoes and other fruit, is devoid of any vitamin A activity.

Vitamin A occurs in animal fats and oils as the fatty acid ester which, however, is readily hydrolysed by enzymes (esterases) of the small intestine. It is absorbed much more readily than the carotenes.

* As much as 1 per cent of the total weight of the halibut's liver is due to Vitamin A.

Both these types of compounds are fairly stable and are not destroyed by cooking or tinning processes, although drastic treatment such as roasting may do so. The vitamin is stored mainly in the liver where a large excess of it is present combined with palmitic acid. It is in this organ too that the carotenes are converted to vitamin A and since this reaction is inhibited in liver disease, a yellow discoloration of the skin due to excess carotene deposition may occur in this condition.

Vitamin A deficiency.

A lack of vitamin A results in night blindness a loss of weight, and a decreased resistance to infections. This last effect is indirect, for the vitamin itself plays no part in fighting the invading bacteria, but is required to maintain the various secretory membranes lining the alimentary tract, the eyes and other organs in their normal healthy condition.

In the absence of the vitamin, there is a general drying up and scale formation (keratinization) of epithelial tissues, including the skin which becomes rough, resembling toad skin. The tear glands too are affected and may result in the eye condition known as xerophthalmia in which the no longer protected eye surface is attacked by bacteria. White deposits are formed in the cornea and conjunctiva of the eye often followed by bleeding and ulceration, from which total blindness may result. It has also been found that pigs from vitamin A deficient sows are often born blind.

Vitamin A deficiency can also lead to reproductive disorders, lesions of the nervous system and retardation of bone growth and tooth formation. However, one of the first symptoms to be observed is night blindness, and the biochemical reasons for this are now fairly well understood.

Night blindness.

The retina which is the part of the eye chiefly concerned with the reception of visual stimuli is composed of two types of cells, the cones responsible for colour vision in fairly bright conditions and the rods for vision in dim light. A pigment-protein complex present in these rods called visual purple or rhodopsin, is responsible for this twilight vision and is bleached by light with the release of retinene, closely allied to vitamin A. It is in fact, the aldehyde form of the vitamin (which is an alcohol) and to which it is converted by a reduction involving $NADH_2$ and the enzyme retinene reductase.

In darkness visual purple is regenerated.

In vitamin A deficiency, less visual purple is available resulting in a decreased ability to adapt and see properly in dim light (night blindness).

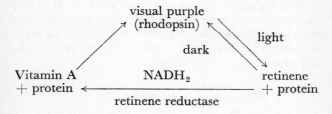

In the retinal rods of certain fresh water fishes, a substance called porphyropsin replaces rhodopsin, and on reduction is converted to vitamin A_2. It is closely related in chemical structure to vitamin A (also called vitamin A_1) which is present in the rods of marine fishes and the higher vertebrates.

Vitamin A toxicity.

There have been reports that excess of vitamin A can be harmful and lead to nausea, weakness and inflammation of the skin. This may be the reason why polar bear liver, which is extremely rich in this vitamin, is poisonous.

THE VITAMIN B COMPLEX

Originally, it was thought that only one water-soluble vitamin existed, namely the one which cured beriberi in man, but later the multiple nature of " vitamin B " was revealed as new biologically active compounds were isolated from the original mixture. They were called vitamin B_1, B_2, B_3, etc. but not all members of this vitamin B complex are essential in human nutrition.

Thiamine (vitamin B_1).

Thiamine is a white crystalline compound freely soluble in water which has the distinction of being the first recognized vitamin (Funk 1911). However, it was not until many years later that the pure compound was finally isolated and its complex structure determined. The total synthesis of this vitamin has now also been accomplished.

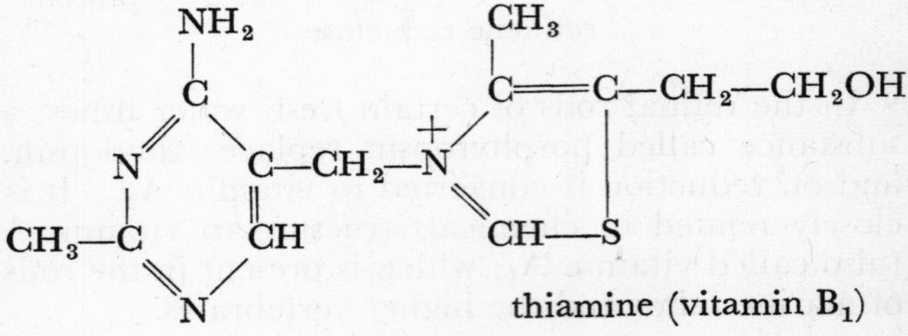

thiamine (vitamin B_1)

It is found in yeast, eggs, liver, pork, cereals and certain vegetables and though it is fairly resistant to heat, it is destroyed by roasting or by pressure cooking. Heating vegetables with boiling water and then discarding the water results in loss of this vitamin as does the milling process used in refining cereals.

Deficiency symptoms.

The disease beriberi, which exists in severe form only in the Orient where severe malnutrition is prevalent, is seen in a modified form in many other parts of the world.

The effect is mainly on the nervous system and the symptoms are weakness, fatigue, headaches, loss of appetite and vague aches and pains in various parts of the body. In severe cases, there is paralysis, oedema (filling of tissues with fluid resulting in a general swelling of the body) and heart failure.

Function.

It has already been mentioned in Chapter IV that the phosphate of vitamin B_1 is cocarboxylase, the coenzyme involved in decarboxylation and the further oxidation of pyruvic acid.

Riboflavin (vitamin B_2).

Riboflavin, another B vitamin of fairly complex structure is the prosthetic group of several dehydrogenases which play such an important part in biological oxidation (see Chapter V). Like thiamine it must combine with phosphoric acid in the body before it can function as a coenzyme. It is an orange yellow compound made up of the reduced pentose sugar ribitol and the dimethyl form of a nitrogen containing compound—isoalloxazine.

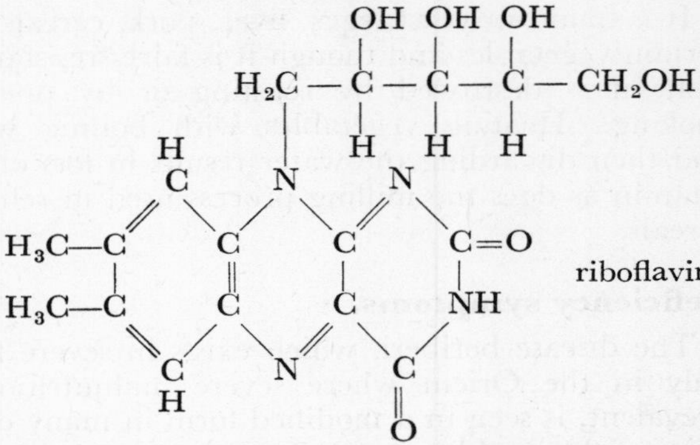

$$H_2C - C - C - C - CH_2OH$$

riboflavin

It is fairly resistant to heat and oxidation and is found in yeast, certain vegetables (turnips and beet tops), liver, kidney, milk and eggs.

Deficiency symptoms.

Lack of riboflavin in the diet results in characteristic lesions of the mouth and eyes, while the skin in certain regions can also be affected. The lips, mouth and tongue are usually sore and there is discomfort in eating and swallowing. The eyes too either " burn " or itch and are bloodshot. The reddening, lesions and ulceration of the lips and corners of the mouth is known as cheilosis and the inflammation of the tongue—glossitis.

Nicotinic acid.

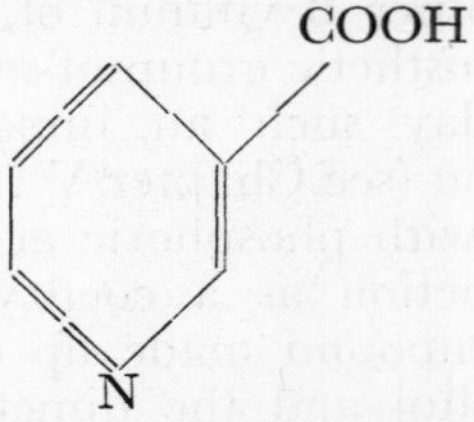

COOH

This vitamin is a white crystalline solid, stable to

heat and found in liver, yeast, milk, eggs and cereals. It is a constituent of NAD and NADP which are important carriers in oxidation systems (see Chapter V). A deficiency of nicotinic acid leads to pellagra but it is believed that a lack of the other vitamins of the B complex and of dietary protein may also be contributive factors.

This deficiency disease, which naturally occurs only in areas of great poverty and hence malnutrition, is characterized by skin, gastro-intestinal and nervous (including mental) disturbances.

The nicotine present in tobacco cannot be converted by smokers to nicotinic acid although the two compounds are chemically related.

Vitamin B_{12}.

This member of the vitamin B series whose complex structure was one of the last to be elucidated contains the element cobalt and is found mainly in the liver. Together with *folic acid*, another vitamin

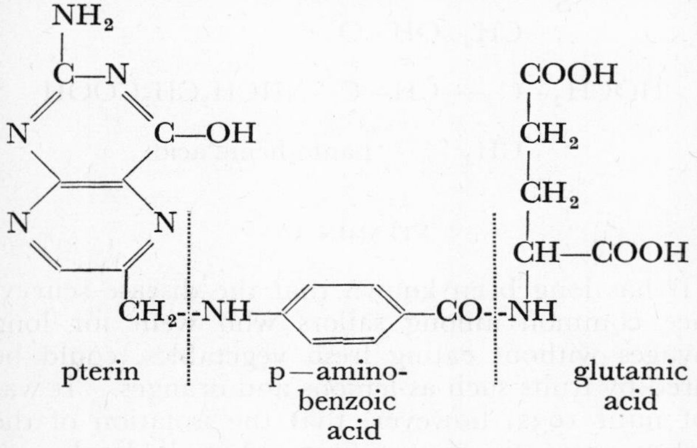

pterin   p—amino-   glutamic
          benzoic   acid
          acid

Folic acid

of the B complex, it plays an important role in preventing pernicious anaemia.

Other members of the vitamin B complex include *pyridoxine* which participates in transamination (see Chapter IX), *biotin* which is important in fatty acid synthesis (see Chapter VIII), and *pantothenic acid*, a component of coenzyme A (see Chapter VII).

$$\text{HO} \begin{array}{c} \text{CH}_2\text{OH} \\ \\ \text{CH}_2\text{OH} \end{array}$$

$$\text{H}_3\text{C} \quad \text{N} \qquad \text{pyridoxine}$$

$$\begin{array}{c} \text{O} \\ \parallel \\ \text{C} \\ \text{HN} \qquad \text{NH} \\ \text{HC}\text{---}\text{CH} \qquad \text{biotin} \\ \text{H}_2\text{C} \qquad \text{CHCH}_2\text{CH}_2\text{CH}_2\text{CH}_2\text{COOH} \\ \text{S} \end{array}$$

$$\begin{array}{c} \text{CH}_3 \quad \text{OH} \quad \text{O} \\ \mid \qquad \mid \qquad \parallel \\ \text{HOCH}_2\text{---}\text{C}\text{---}\text{CH}\text{---}\text{C}\text{---}\text{NHCH}_2\text{CH}_2\text{COOH} \\ \mid \\ \text{CH}_3 \qquad \text{pantothenic acid} \end{array}$$

VITAMIN C

It has long been known that the disease scurvy, once common among sailors who went for long voyages without eating fresh vegetables, could be cured by fruits such as lemons and oranges. It was not until 1932, however, that the isolation of the scurvy preventive agent from adrenal glands and also cabbage leaves was announced.

It was given the name vitamin C or ascorbic acid, and it is a sugar-like compound which is easily oxidized to inactive dehydroascorbic acid.

$$
\begin{array}{ccc}
\begin{array}{c}
\mathrm{O{=}C} \\
\mathrm{HO{-}C} \\
\mathrm{HO{-}C} \\
\mathrm{H{-}C} \\
\mathrm{HO{-}C{-}H} \\
\mathrm{CH_2OH}
\end{array} \Big]\mathrm{O}
&
\xrightarrow[\text{$-2H$}]{\text{oxidation}}
&
\begin{array}{c}
\mathrm{O{=}C} \\
\mathrm{O{=}C} \\
\mathrm{O{=}C} \\
\mathrm{H{-}C} \\
\mathrm{HO{-}C{-}H} \\
\mathrm{CH_2OH}
\end{array} \Big]\mathrm{O}
\\
\text{ascorbic} & & \text{dehydroascorbic} \\
\text{acid} & & \text{acid}
\end{array}
$$

It is common in all fresh fruits, especially black currants, oranges, lemons and grapefruits and is also found in green vegetables and potatoes. A large proportion of the vitamin is destroyed by cooking and this process is accelerated by traces of the element copper, present in many cooking utensils.

Vitamin C, like riboflavin and nicotinic acid, is concerned with biological oxidation and an enzyme, ascorbic oxidase present in many plants as well as in the adrenal glands catalyzes its conversion to dehydroascorbic acid. It can reduce —S—S— groups to —SH groups in the body and it has also been found to decrease the toxic effect of certain drugs. As mentioned earlier, only man, apes and guinea pigs require a dietary supply of ascorbic acid since other animal species can synthesize this vitamin from carbohydrate.

Deficiency symptoms.

A deficiency of ascorbic acid results in the disease scurvy which is characterized by weakness, sore spongy gums and a tendency for bleeding in the muscles and internal organs. There are also degenerative changes in bones and cartilage and the healing of wounds is greatly impaired. All these symptoms are rapidly cured on administering either the pure vitamin or food containing it.

VITAMIN D

This vitamin is not a single dietary factor but a group of closely related steroids (see Chapter VIII) found in association with vitamin A in fish liver oils, eggs and milk. One of the most active members of the group is calciferol or vitamin D_2 which has been isolated in the pure crystalline state and can be formed by ultra violet irradiation of ergosterol, a compound closely related to cholesterol. (See Chapter VIII).

calciferol

Whereas vitamin D_2 and ergosterol are essentially plant products, vitamin D_3 which is formed by the action of sunlight on 7-dehydrocholesterol, is of animal origin only. Like ergosterol, 7-dehydrocholesterol is a provitamin because it can be converted to an active substance but has no effect itself. It is present in skin, which accounts for the beneficial action of sunshine in preventing rickets (see below) and the prevalence of this disease in the past in the slums of industrial cities.

Deficiency symptoms.

Vitamin D has a marked effect on calcium and inorganic phosphate metabolism, and these two substances are essential for normal bone formation.

A lack of vitamin A causes rickets, a disease of children, in which the bones become soft due to insufficient deposition of calcium phosphate resulting in knock-knees, bow-legs and other skeletal malformations.

In adults, vitamin D deficiency causes osteomalacia, which is a modified form of rickets usually seen only in pregnancy. The vitamin also plays an important role in the formation of teeth, but it will not prevent dental caries.

Vitamin D toxicity.

Vitamin D given in very large amounts can be toxic and lead to the deposition of calcium phosphate from the bones to abnormal sites in the body including the blood vessels. With the exception of A and D, all other vitamins, as far as is known, can be given in excess without any harmful effects.

VITAMIN E

This fat-soluble vitamin which is present in wheat

germ, and lettuce leaves, as well as in eggs and milk, is required for normal breeding in rats but whether it is essential to man is not yet known for certain.

Vitamin E deficiency results in atrophy of the testes in male rats, and in the female, although ovulation and fertilization occur, the foetuses die in the uterus and are resorbed.

Vitamin E is a yellow oil that is readily oxidized and it has now been synthesized in the laboratory.

VITAMIN K

Vitamin K which is also known as the coagulation or anti-haemorrhagic vitamin, is required for the formation in the liver of prothrombin, a compound essential for normal blood clotting (see Chapter IX). It is present mainly in green plants especially in the lucerne and spinach and a certain amount of it is synthesized in the intestine by bacteria.

Newborn infants may show symptoms of vitamin K deficiency but these persist only until the establishment of a bacterial flora in the intestine. The administration of vitamin K to pregnant women before childbirth has decreased the incidence of this condition.

Two separate compounds, Vitamin K_1 and K_2, are now known to exist, and the former has the following structure:

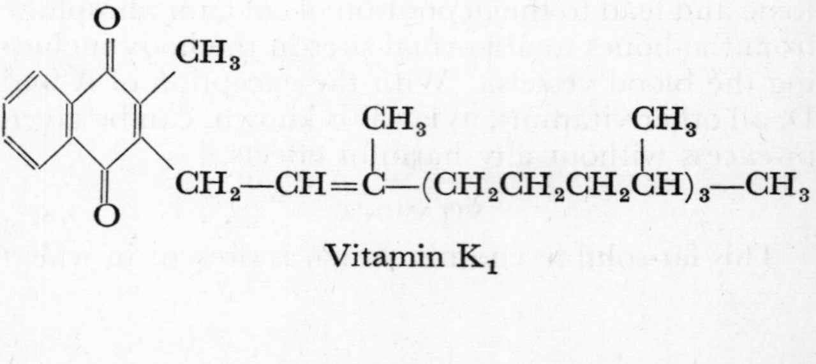

Vitamin K_1

A number of synthetic compounds with vitamin K activity are known and one of the most potent members of this group is menadione.

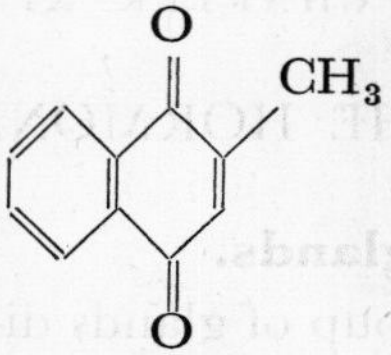

menadione

CHAPTER XI

THE HORMONES

The Endocrine glands.

THE endocrine group of glands differ from others in the body such as salivary and sweat glands in that they are without ducts and pour their secretions directly into the blood. They contain substances known as hormones which may be proteins, steroids or relatively simple organic substances and which are carried to all parts of the body thus acting as chemical messengers.

They act very rapidly and like the enzymes and vitamins even minute amounts can have a profound effect on metabolism. This has been shown experimentally by injecting the hormone into an animal from which the gland producing that particular hormone had previously been removed and which therefore was showing characteristic deficiency symptoms.

The endocrine glands and their location in the body are shown in the figure opposite and though the hormones produced by each of these organs will be discussed separately it must be realized that a very complicated interaction exists between all of them. It is often very hard to know whether the effect of an injected hormone is due to it as such or whether it merely stimulates another endocrine gland to produce hormones which, in turn, may stimulate yet other glands. Nevertheless, through much research, it has been possible to allocate a definite

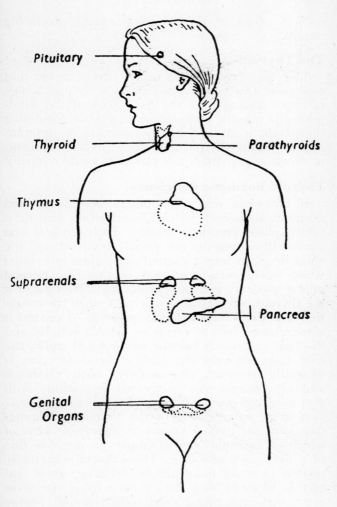

The Endocrine Glands

role to many of these vital hormone producing organs.

The Thyroid

This gland is located in the neck region and consists of two lobes connected by a narrow bridge of tissue passing over the front part of the windpipe. It plays a very important role in regulating the metabolic rate of the body and marked symptoms appear during thyroid deficiency (hypothyroidism) or excessive activity of this gland (hyperthyroidism).

Thyroid hormone deficiency.

If for some reason or other there is thyroid hormone deficiency in childhood while growth is taking place, cretinism results. Both physical and mental developments are greatly retarded and the child develops into a stunted pot-bellied individual whose intelligence at 30 may be that of a normal person aged 5. If deficiency occurs in later life or if the thyroid is removed at this stage, then the condition known as myxoedema develops. This too is accompanied by a decrease in mental activity and the face and hands become swollen and puffy, the hair falls out and the body's metabolic rate is generally reduced. Fortunately, both cretinism and myxoedema can be treated successfully with thyroid gland preparations or thyroid hormone. A great enlargement of the thyroid is characteristic of the disease known as goitre one form of which—" endemic " or " simple " goitre—is due to a deficiency of iodine. This element is normally present in small quantities in drinking water and certain types of food (e.g. marine fish). In these cases, however, there is usually enough iodine present (the thyroid hormone contains this element) to prevent the appearance of symptoms of hypo-thyroidism.

This form of goitre can be cured readily by adding sodium iodide to table salt or to the drinking water and such measures have been adopted in certain regions of Switzerland and North America where the condition used to be relatively common.

In normal individuals too, the thyroid hormone will produce a marked rise in the metabolic rate shown by quickening of the pulse, increased appetite and decrease in body fat. The hormone will also accelerate the metamorphosis of tadpoles into adult frogs and this procedure has been used to assay the potency of thyroid hormone preparations.

Hyperthyroidism.

The thyroid gland also increases in size in cases of exophthalmic goitre or Graves' disease, but in this case there is an excess of the hormone produced so that the metabolic rate is raised. A very characteristic symptom of this disease, from which the word exophthalmic originates, is the bulging of the eyes. The pulse is very fast and muscular tremors and weakness may be present. Certain " goitro-genic " substances (see below) have been used in the treatment of this disease and iodide too may have a beneficial effect. Sometimes, however, part or the whole of the gland has to be removed and, in the latter case, thyroid hormone is administered for the rest of the patient's life.

The thyroid hormones.

The active hormone, thyroxine, which is a rela-tively simple iodine containing compound derived from the amino acid tyrosine, is found in the thyroid combined with protein as thyroglobulin.

Most of the hormone is manufactured in the thyroid which has a remarkable affinity for iodine, but small amounts may be formed in other parts of the body.

When radioactive iodine is given to an animal, the radioactivity is found to be mainly in the thyroid and is present there first as the free element. Later it appears in the di-iodotyrosine and lastly in the thyroxine of the gland, which suggests that the active hormone is formed from tyrosine via di-iodotyrosine.

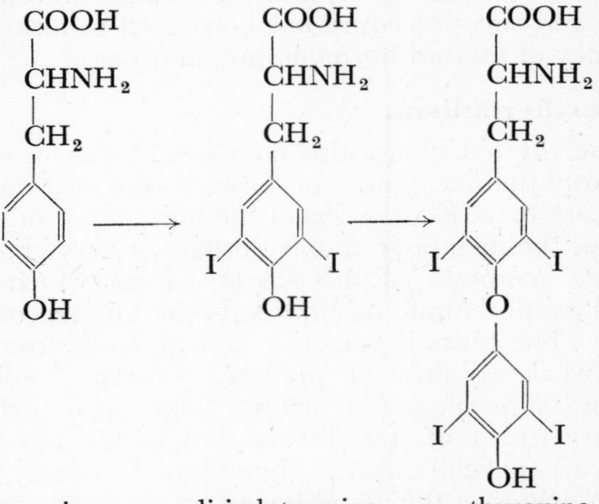

tyrosine   di-iodotyrosine   thyroxine

Mono-iodotyrosine has also been found after hydrolysis of the thyroid gland but both this compound and the di-iodo derivative are very much less active than thyroxine. More recently, tri-iodo-thyronine (thyroxine with only 3 iodine atoms) has been detected and found to be highly active. Several other compounds, not found naturally, such as the nitrophenols can simulate the thyroid hormone in raising the metabolic rate but they cannot cure either cretinism or myxoedema.

It is also interesting to note that when proteins such as casein of milk are treated with iodine in the laboratory the product is thyroid active, and both di-iodotyrosine and thyroxine are liberated on hydrolysis.

The thyroid is stimulated by the thyrotropic hormone of the anterior pituitary, and because extracts of this gland on injection give rise to exophthalmic symptoms, it is believed that excess of the thyrotropic hormone may be responsible for this form of goitre.

Goitrogenic substances.

Following the observation that rabbits maintained for long periods mainly on cabbage leaves or turnip seeds developed a form of goitre, it was found that certain substances could counteract the effects of thyroid hormone. Thiourea, thiouracil and methyl thiouracil are some of the more active compounds with antithyroid properties and have been used clinically in the treatment of hyperthyroidism (exophthalmic goitre).

thiouracil   thiourea

The Parathyroid.

Lying by the side of the thyroid are four small glands, the parathyroids, which play a very important role in regulating calcium and phosphorus metabolism. The hormone it produces—parathormone—is a protein and it cannot therefore be given by mouth because it would be digested and inactivated by the proteolytic enzymes of the alimentary tract.

Removal or injury of the parathyroids results in a rapid fall in the level of blood calcium which is accompanied by the onset of tetany, characterized by a stiffening of the muscles, convulsions and death. Severe vitamin D deficiency can also result in tetany and, like parathormone, this vitamin is able to raise the level of calcium in blood.

In hyperparathyroidism, calcium is removed from the bones which become susceptible to fractures and the concentration of this element in blood is raised. Insoluble calcium deposits are formed in the soft tissues and may give rise to kidney stones with impairment of renal function.

The Islets of Langerhans.

The pancreas, as well as secreting digestive juices, which are carried by ducts to the intestine, also has special cells, collectively known as the islets of Langerhans, which function as an endocrine gland because they pour their product directly into the blood stream. They are responsible for manufacturing the hormone, insulin, which plays an important role in regulating the concentration of glucose in blood (see Chapter VII). Injury or malfunction of these cells results in sugar diabetes.

The thymus gland.

This gland, found behind the breast bone, is present only in children though traces of it remain in the adult.   Very little is known about its function as an endocrine gland, and it is thought to be concerned with growth and sexual maturation. It is now known to play an important role in the development of those cells in the body which are involved in antibody formation.

Enlargement of the thymus has been found in cases of myasthenia gravis, an obscure disease characterized by marked muscular weakness. Removal of the thymus has often benefited patients with this condition.

The pituitary gland.

This small gland, situated at the base of the skull, may be divided functionally into an anterior and a posterior part and it is a very important endocrine organ.   It has great influence over all the other hormone producing glands of the body and has, in fact, been called " the conductor of the endocrine orchestra ".

The anterior pituitary.

This portion of the gland is responsible for most of the effects associated with the pituitary as a whole and the several hormones produced by it are all proteins or smaller polypeptides. There is still some confusion about how many active agents are really present because one hormone may have more than one physiological role but the following are now generally accepted:

1) growth hormone
2) thyrotropic hormone
3) adrenocorticotropic hormone
4) lactogenic hormone
5) gonadotropic hormones

In humans, underactivity of the anterior pituitary is known as Simmonds' disease, characterized by rapidly developing senile decay. Thus, the hair turns grey, the skin becomes wrinkled and dry, the teeth fall out and there is emaciation, mental deterioration and loss of sexual function.

The excessive production of anterior pituitary hormones gives rise to gigantism, acromegaly and Cushing's disease (see below).

1) *Growth hormone.*

Removal of the anterior pituitary from young animals results in cessation of growth and sexual development whereas overactivity of the gland or injections of large amounts of the hormone causes gigantism. In many human giants, often between 7–8 feet tall, an abnormally large pituitary gland has been shown by x-ray examination and in experiments with the hormone, rats $1\frac{1}{2}$ times normal size have been reared.

In the adult, excess of the hormone results in the condition known as acromegaly, characterized by renewed growth of parts of the skeleton especially the hands, feet and the jaw. The blood sugar level too is raised and permanent sugar diabetes may develop. The increase in blood glucose concentration that follows removal of the pancreas, which is the source of insulin, is not as marked in the absence of the anterior pituitary. It is obvious therefore that this gland also plays a very important role in carbohydrate metabolism, but although originally it was thought that a separate blood sugar raising (diabetogenic) hormone was responsible for this effect, it is now known to be due to growth hormone, and ACTH (see below).

2) *Thyrotropic hormone*.

Removal of the pituitary results in atrophy of the thyroid gland with consequent lowering of the metabolic rate, whereas administration of pituitary extracts improves this condition. This effect is due to the thyrotropic hormone which, it will be remembered, can even give rise to the symptoms of exophthalmic goitre when given in excess.

3) *Adrenocorticotropic hormone* (ACTH).

Just as the thyrotropic hormone stimulates the thyroid so this hormone has a stimulatory effect on the cortical part (outer layer) of the adrenal gland. ACTH is used in the treatment of rheumatoid arthritis and it acts by enhancing the production of cortisone and related substances by the adrenal glands. The amino acid composition and sequence of ACTH, which is a polypeptide containing 39 amino acids, is now well established.

Overproduction of ACTH results in Cushing's disease, the main features of which are obesity of the trunk, face and buttocks but not of the limbs, pigmentation of the skin, excessive growth of hair (women may grow a moustache or beard), acne and loss of sexual function.

4) *Lactogenic hormone*.

This pituitary hormone, also called prolactin, is essential for the initiation and maintenance of lactation. During pregnancy, the placenta* produces oestrogens and progesterone which stimulate the growth of the breasts and also inhibit the action of prolactin until after childbirth.

---

* Special mass of tissue which forms the main connection between mother and child and which ensures that the latter's nutritional, respiratory and excretory requirements are satisfied.

Prolactin will arouse maternal instinct in virgin rats and induce broodiness in hens.

5) *Gonadotropic hormone*.

The gonadotropic hormones have a stimulating effect on the sex gland (gonads) and removal of the pituitary gland results in atrophy of these structures in the adult and in failure to mature in younger individuals.

Another gonadotropic hormone is produced by the placenta and enough of it appears in the urine about one month after conception to permit its detection by biological assay. This is the basis of the Aschheim–Zondek (A/Z) test for pregnancy.

The posterior pituitary.

Two active substances, vasopressin and oxytocin, are known to be produced by the posterior lobe of the pituitary. The former raises the blood pressure and reduces the secretion of urine whereas the latter causes contraction of plain muscle such as is found in the uterus and therefore plays an important part in determining the onset of labour.

Vasopressin will lower the tremendous output of urine (10–30 litres per day) which occurs during the disease diabetes insipidus (not to be confused with diabetes mellitus or sugar diabetes).

Vasopressin and oxytocin are each made up of 9 amino acids and they have both been synthesized in the laboratory.

The adrenal gland.

The adrenal glands are two small glands lying on top of the kidneys and consist of two parts, an inner medulla, and an outer cortex surrounding it.

The medulla.

This part of the adrenal secretes the hormone adrenaline which resembles the amino acid tyrosine chemically and from which, in fact, it is derived in the body.

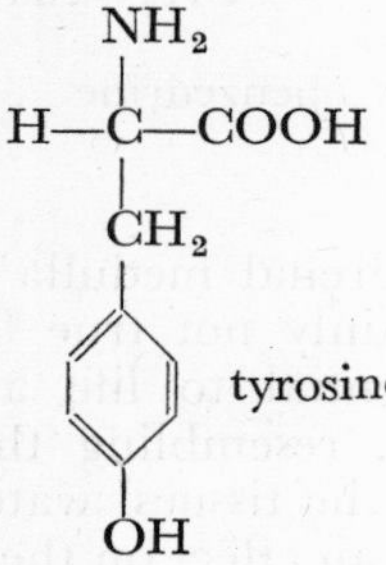

tyrosine

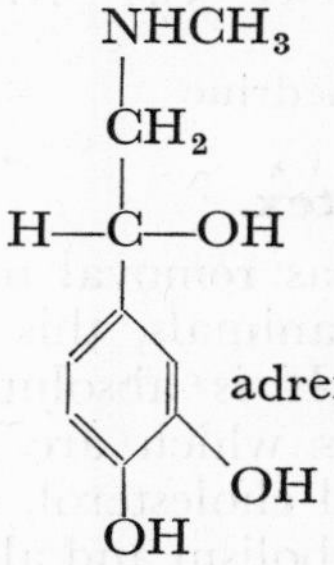

adrenaline

Adrenaline has a marked effect in constricting the blood vessels and stimulating the rate and force of contraction of the heart, thus raising the blood pressure. It also raises the blood sugar level at the expense of liver glycogen by activating liver phosphorylase (see Chapter VII), and it makes the pupils of the eyes expand and hair stand on end. In fact, this hormone, which is liberated in excess in response to some grave emergency, prepares the body for " fight " or " flight ".

The injection of adrenaline results in the same reactions as those which occur when the sympathetic nervous system is stimulated.

The physiological properties of adrenaline have made it useful in the treatment of shock and collapse as well as in the prevention of bleeding. The hormone is fairly rapidly destroyed when given by mouth but a number of closely related compounds are known, which although less active, exert their effect over a longer period. These include ephedrine, which occurs naturally in the plant, ephedra vulgaris, and the synthetic compound, benzedrine.

ephedrine   benzedrine

The cortex.

Whereas removal of the adrenal medulla is not fatal to animals, this is certainly not true for the cortex. It is absolutely essential to life and its hormones which are steroids, resembling the bile acids and cholesterol, control the tissues' water and salt metabolism and also have an effect on the blood sugar level. A large number of these hormones have now been isolated in pure crystalline form and cortisone, which has a beneficial effect in rheumatoid arthritis and certain allergies may be taken as a typical example.

cortisone

Other members of this group include corticosterone and cortisol, the main adrenal steroids in mammalian blood, and aldosterone which causes the retention of sodium and elimination of potassium from the body.

Adrenocortical hormone deficiency is known as Addison's disease, and all the symptoms as well as those observed when the adrenals are removed from animals can be cured by giving adrenal extracts. Common salt (NaCl) in the diet has a marked beneficial effect, but potassium salts aggravate the condition. It must also be remembered that pituitary ACTH plays an important role by stimulating the production of adrenocortical hormones.

The adrenal cortex as well as the sex glands are known to produce sex hormones.

The sex hormones.

Like the adrenocortical hormones the substances secreted by the sex glands (gonads) are steroids and they control the development of the genital organs and the secondary sexual characteristics. These include hairiness, deep voice and narrow hips in men and the opposite attributes as well as the development of breasts in women. Those hormones which are responsible for the male secondary sexual characteristics are known as androgens and those controlling the female secondary sexual characteristics—oestrogens. Since the adrenal cortex of each sex also produces both these types of hormone, overactivity of the gland (e.g. in adrenal tumour) can result in masculinization of women with growth of hair over the face and body or else feminization of men with the development of breasts.

The androgens.

The testes are responsible for the production of much of the body's chief androgen—testosterone, a white crystalline compound of known structure.

testosterone | androsterone

Androgenic activity can be determined by the comb-growth test in which the substance to be tested is injected into a capon (castrated cockerel) and the amount of comb growth measured. Both testosterone and androsterone can be synthesized in the body as well as in the laboratory from cholesterol.

The oestrogens.

In a large number of mammalian species the female is only ready to mate during certain periods, when she is in oestrus (on " heat "). These rhythmic changes do not occur in sexually immature animals or in those with their ovaries removed, and an oestrogen is defined as a substance which when injected into such animals will bring them into oestrus.

Two important oestrogenic substances produced mainly in the ovaries are oestradiol and its metabolite, oestrone.

They are responsible for the female secondary sexual characteristics and they also control the growth of uterine tissue.

A third oestrogen, oestriol, is found in relatively large quantities in human pregnancy urine. The placenta too is known to form oestrogens.

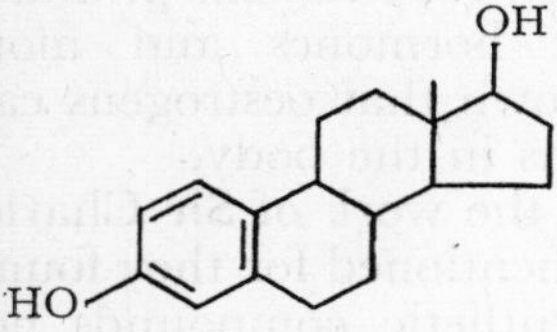

oestradiol

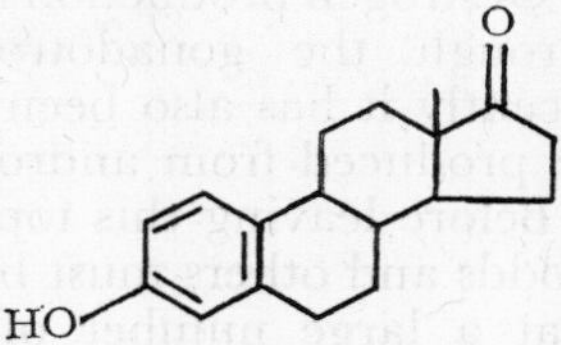

oestrone

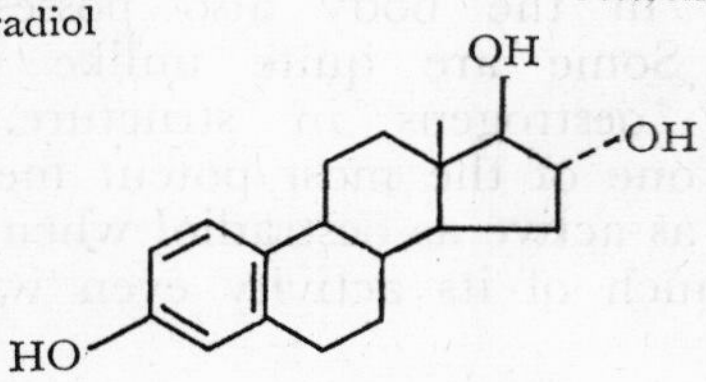

oestriol

Another important steroid hormone, progesterone, is produced by the yellow " body " or corpus luteum of the ovary which develops after ovulation and which reaches considerable size after fertilization of the ovum. The oestrogens, together with progesterone, play an important role in maintaining pregnancy and their excretion in the urine reaches a peak value just before birth.

Progesterone is found in the urine in its reduced form—pregnanediol.

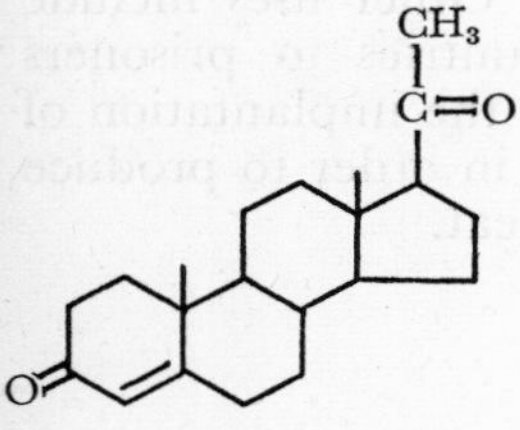

progesterone

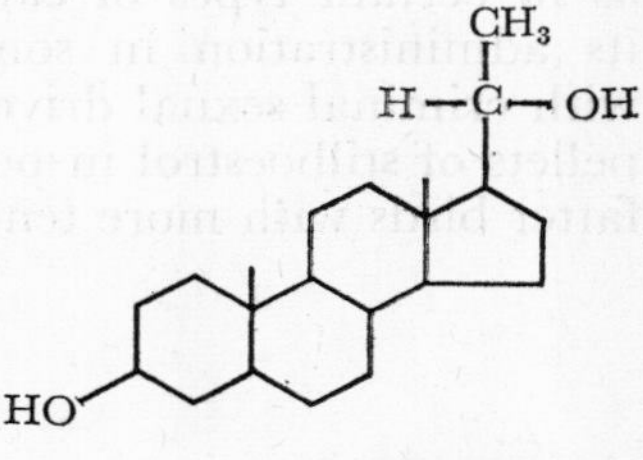

pregnanediol

M

Oestrogen production is controlled by the pituitary through the gonadotropic hormones and more recently it has also been shown that oestrogens can be produced from androgens in the body.

Before leaving this topic, the work of Sir Charles Dodds and others must be mentioned for they found that a large number of synthetic compounds not occurring in the body also possess oestrogenic activity. Some are quite unlike the naturally occurring oestrogens in structure. Stilboestrol, which is one of the most potent members of this group, is as active as oestradiol when injected, and retains much of its activity even when given by mouth.

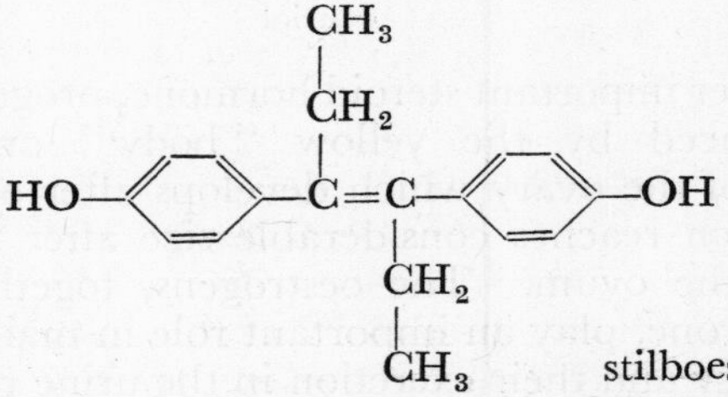

$$
\text{HO} - \underset{}{\bigcirc} - \underset{\substack{CH_2 \\ | \\ CH_3}}{\overset{\substack{CH_3 \\ | \\ CH_2}}{C}} = C - \underset{}{\bigcirc} - \text{OH}
$$

stilboestrol

It has been used clinically in the treatment of delayed puberty, the suppression of lactation on weaning and the treatment of the menopause as well as in certain types of cancer. Other uses include its administration in some countries to prisoners with criminal sexual drive, and the implantation of pellets of stilboestrol in poultry in order to produce fatter birds with more tender meat.

CHAPTER XII

THE BIOCHEMISTRY OF CANCER

PERHAPS no single disease has aroused such universal interest and anxiety as cancer and though much is known about this disease, very much more research is needed before the final battle against it is won and its heavy toll of human life checked. To the biochemist it presents many interesting problems and the challenge has been taken up.

Cancer has been recognized as a grave disease since antiquity, but because in those days the expectancy of life was very short and because cancer occurs generally late in life, it never attained the same importance then as in modern times.

After diseases of the heart, cancer is the commonest of the fatal diseases and about one person in eight eventually dies from it.

It is of interest that even extinct prehistoric animals like the dinosaurs suffered from cancer as is clearly shown in fossilized skeletons.

Malignancy.

One of the most extraordinary phenomena in nature is the repeated division of a single fertilized egg to give rise to the orderly mass of cells which form the different tissues of the body. The remarkable similarity between identical twins further emphasizes this orderliness in development.

At first the cells still look alike and are called primitive or embryonic but with continued growth certain groups of them begin to show structural modifications and eventually give rise to the different tissues. Thus the liver is made up of certain types of cells, the kidneys from another set and each one on dividing will give rise to cells of its own particular kind. These cells are said to be differentiated.

In the adult, cell division still proceeds even after actual growth has ceased, for new tissues have to be formed to replace the old ones lost through general wear and tear, and this regenerative ability of the body depends on the age of the individual.

In certain cases however, the dividing cells "run amok" and grow rapidly in a disorderly fashion penetrating and destroying indiscriminately the surrounding tissues. These cells are then said to be malignant and the reason for this transformation which apparently cannot be reversed, is one of the main problems of cancer.

The malignant cells have a remarkable ability for growing in tissues, quite unlike the ones from which they originate, unlike normal cells, which usually die if they are transplanted to other sites in the body.

A tumour is an abnormal growth often composed of malignant cells, which, if detached from the main mass, are carried by the circulation to different parts of the body to form new growths called secondary or metastic tumours. Even though the primary mass of cancer cells may have started growing in a non-vital area of the body, the secondary tumours may develop in organs which are absolutely essential thus causing the death of the individual. Since cells which have metastasized often revert to their primitive form, it may be hard to determine the primary site of origin of a secondary tumour.

Collectively the malignant cells are easily recognized because they penetrate other tissues and are often more primitive than the surrounding normal cells, but a single cancer cell when viewed under the microscope may appear quite normal in general structure. These cells also have the same kind of enzymes as normal ones though there are often small differences in the relative amounts of certain of these biocatalysts.

Malignant tumours must not be confused with benign ones which are abnormal but relatively harmless growths such as warts for example. They can become dangerous, however, if they press on some vital organ. The cells of benign tumours do not develop rapidly without regard to the host, penetrating and destroying neighbouring tissues, nor do they metastasize. In addition, they cannot be transplanted successfully into another member of the same species, whereas malignant cells will grow and multiply under these conditions.

Malignant growths can occur in plants as well as in animals and the so-called " crown galls " can be transplanted and will even metastasize.

A normal cell may become malignant under the stimulus of a number of different agents which may be physical, chemical or biological. Although most of these factors, such as radiation, tar and various industrial chemicals arise from outside and are foreign to the cells, some may be produced by the body itself. Before dealing with these, however, some general facts about cancer should be considered.

Incidence of cancer.

It has already been mentioned that one person in eight dies of cancer, that it is second on the list of killing diseases and that it occurs in many types of animals as well as in humans.

The question has recently arisen whether there is

an increasing tendency for this disease to develop in man. The answer is problematical because although more people die from it nowadays, life expectancy has risen greatly so that more people survive to acquire cancer.

Methods of finding deep-lying tumours have also improved greatly and a few decades ago many deaths due to cancer may have been given a different diagnosis.

The incidence differs in men and women mainly in the regions affected. Thus, in men, cancer commonly involves the digestive tract, the lungs and the prostate, whereas in women the generative system and the breasts are the most frequent sites.

The influence of heredity.

It is not possible to give a definite answer as to whether cancer is hereditary in human beings although it seems that there is some predisposition to acquire the disease which is inherited. In mice, it has been shown by using highly inbred strains obtained by repeated brother–sister mating, that certain of these breeds have a much greater tendency to acquire the disease than others. However, since a large number of factors influence the onset of malignancy and since human life and behaviour is extremely complicated and variable, it cannot be proved conclusively that heredity for cancer operates in man. Even though it probably does, there is so little intermarriage that for all practical purposes the problem does not arise.

As far as is known, cancer is not contagious but there is some evidence that diet may play a role in inducing malignant growths in man in certain parts of the world. More recently, it has been shown that smoking is one of the causes of lung cancer.

Treatment.

Though very little is known about the reasons for normal cells becoming malignant, it is incorrect to assume that cancer is incurable, except when it is recognized too late.   One major difference between cancer and other diseases is that in the latter case, the body plays the main part in defending itself whereas in cancer the body is quite helpless.   In fact, it nourishes the tumour at the expense of other tissues instead of destroying it.

The removal by surgery of the primary tumour before it has started producing secondaries is one of the two main methods of treatment, and it is essential in this case to make sure that not a single malignant cell remains behind.   Unless this condition is fulfilled, a new tumour will soon grow and ultimately kill the patient.   This method therefore needs skill on the part of the surgeon and unfortunately, large areas may have to be removed in order to ensure the complete elimination of malignant tissue.

The other main type of treatment consists of irradiating the tumour with either x-rays, or γ-rays from highly radioactive elements such as radium. Both these rays consist of electromagnetic waves, similar to normal light rays but their wavelength is very much shorter with the result that they are invisible and very penetrating.

It has been found that cancer cells are more vulnerable to these rays than normal cells so that by choosing the right intensity of radiation and focusing the rays on to the part affected, it is possible to destroy the malignant cells without causing too much injury to the surrounding healthy tissues.

The advantage of this method is that it will result in the destruction of outlying malignant cells, scattered amongst normal tissue, without the need to sacrifice the latter as in surgery. Unfortunately radiation treatment is only effective against certain types of cancer and is quite useless against others.

One interesting example of radiation treatment is the use of radioactive iodine for cancer of the thyroid. It has already been mentioned (Chapter XI) that this gland takes up iodine selectively with the result that when the radioactive element is administered, it finds its way to the thyroid where it becomes concentrated and irradiates the malignant cells at close range. Even when the primary thyroid tumour has metastasized and secondaries have formed in different parts of the body, these still retain their affinity for iodine and are destroyed.

There are at present a number of drugs which will selectively kill the malignant cells without having highly toxic effects on the normal tissues as well. However, the cells invariably become resistant to these agents after a period of time, and the tumour then starts growing again. Hormones, and in particular the oestrogens, have been used with great success for cancer of the breast and prostate (a gland situated near the bladder in males).

Extrinsic cancer producing factors.

1) chemicals.

It has long been known that workers in certain occupations were particularly liable to develop certain types of cancer and one of the earliest observations was made back in the 18th century by Sir Percival Pott. He pointed out that cancer of the scrotum (the bag of skin which contains the testicles) was exceptionally common amongst chimney sweeps and suggested that soot was the extrinsic agent responsible for it.

With the development of industry, other occupational causes became apparent. Thus skin cancer was commonly found among workers in coal tar distillation plants or else among those who came into contact with the heavy lubricating oils of machines such as some workers in cotton spinning mills (mulespinners' cancer). Similarly cancer of the bladder was associated with the aniline dye industry.

Coal miners, however, do not suffer from skin cancer for although both soot and tar are products of coal they have been subjected to high temperatures and thus differ from it in their chemical composition.

It seemed therefore very likely that soot, tar and other products were responsible for these various malignant effects and it was decided to obtain additional proof by inducing the same type of cancer in experimental animals. Coal tar was therefore applied repeatedly to the ears of rabbits and a malignant growth was eventually induced. It needed very long and patient application of tar and the choice of experimental animal was unfortunate because the rabbit is exceptionally resistant to this type of induced cancer.

There is a definite species difference in susceptibility to the various cancer inducing substances so that the fact that coal tar produces cancer in rabbits does not prove conclusively that it will also have this effect in man. However, together with the occupational evidence, there is little doubt that humans too are susceptible to these carcinogens and that precautions must be taken.

a) *The Carcinogenic Hydrocarbons.*

Once it was realized that soot and tar were carcinogenic (i.e., capable of giving rise to cancer), a search was started for the active compounds and this eventually met with success. It was found that most of the activity of tar could be accounted for by the presence in it of small amounts of a highly carcinogenic substance—3,4-benzpyrene together with some other polycyclic hydrocarbons (i.e., compounds composed of several benzene nuclei). Many similar hydrocarbons were then synthesized and several shown to be highly active, especially 1,2,5,6-dibenzanthracene.

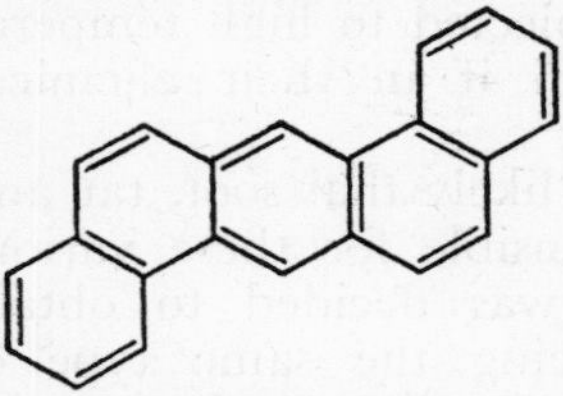

1,2,5,6-dibenzanthracene

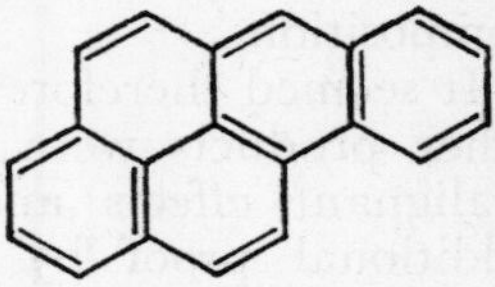

3,4-benzpyrene

Another highly carcinogenic compound, methylcholanthrene, can be synthesized in the laboratory from deoxycholic acid which occurs naturally in bile. It has therefore been suggested that under abnormal conditions a similar conversion of bile acid to an active carcinogen may be one of the causes of cancer, but there is no evidence that this can occur in the body.

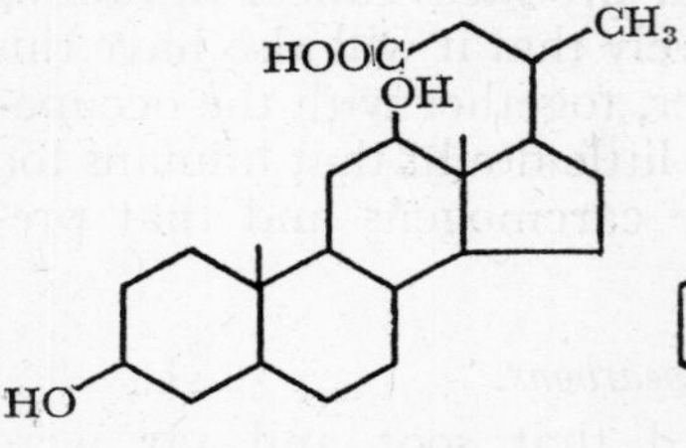

deoxycholic acid

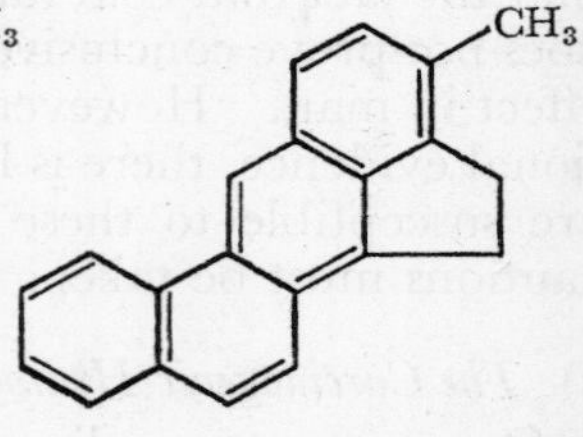

methyl cholanthrene

It is quite possible, however, that the recent increases in lung cancer may be due to some of these hydrocarbons in the soot in the air of the larger industrial cities where much of the population is concentrated.

b) The Azo dyes.

Occupational cancer in the dye industry, led to an investigation of nitrogen-containing compounds on lines similar to the ones adopted for the polycyclic hydrocarbons. It was found that certain azo dyes (i.e. coloured aromatic compounds containing a —N=N— grouping) were highly carcinogenic, and one such compound is butter yellow. This substance causes cancer of the liver (hepatoma) in rats and is converted in the body to p-aminophenol and p-phenylene diamine, neither of which is carcinogenic.

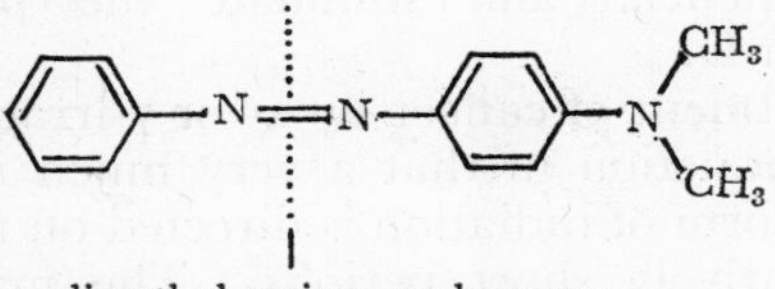

p-dimethyl-amino-azo-benzene

(butter yellow).

p-aminophenol   p-phenylene diamine

A relatively simple nitrogen containing compound which is not an azo dye but produces cancer of the bladder in dogs is β-naphthylamine. It has been shown, however, that one of its metabolites is the real carcinogen.

2) Ultraviolet radiation.

The observation that a relatively high incidence of skin cancer occurred among farmers, fishermen and people exposed for long periods to strong sunlight as well as among the early x-ray workers and those in contact with radioactive compounds led to the conclusion that short wave length radiation could induce cancer.

Further evidence was provided by the fact that malignant diseases of the skin are commonest in countries with much sunshine. It affects fair people more readily than dark ones because the brown pigment, melanin, protects the skin from the ultraviolet rays of the sun.

Precautions must therefore be taken against these rays, though it should be emphasized that only very prolonged exposure to them will induce malignancy and that normal amounts of ultraviolet irradiation are beneficial and stimulate the production of vitamin D.

Treatment of cancer by x- or γ-irradiation differs from induction in that a very much more concentrated form of radiation is directed on to the tumour for relatively short periods. The malignant cells are thus killed preferentially if they are susceptible to this form of treatment.

A reassuring fact is that although both chemicals and ultraviolet radiation can induce cancer, only a very small percentage of people exposed to these extrinsic factors actually get the disease.

3) Hormones.

As early as 1932, it was shown by Lacassagne that the injection of female sex hormones could produce cancer of the breast in mice and later many different types of hormone-induced tumours were discovered. This therefore indicates a direct connection between carcinogenesis and compounds that occur naturally in the body.

The carcinogenic action of hormones is generally confined to those tissues which are normally stimulated by them.

Viruses and cancer.

It was shown many years ago by Rous that a cell-free extract of a chicken tumour would give rise to cancer in normal healthy chickens when injected and he therefore suggested that a virus was responsible.

It has also been demonstrated that when a breed of mice resistant to cancer of the breast are given milk belonging to a breed of mice highly susceptible to breast cancer, then the former will easily develop the disease. This reinforces the view that cancer-producing (oncogenic) viruses might exist and, like viruses in general, they can be divided into two broad classes: those that contain DNA as their genetic material and those that contain RNA. However, while the RNA-containing viruses can be readily found in the tumours to which they give rise, the DNA-containing viruses disappear and cannot be recovered from the tumours. This means that the absence of a virus in a human cancer does not necessarily mean that a virus did not cause it. On the other hand, there are no grounds whatever for believing that all tumours in man or animals are induced by viruses.

INDEX